NUFFIELD SCIENCE *in* PRACTICE

GNVQ SCIENCE

INTERMEDIATE

Heinemann

Contents

Credits

Author and editor of this book
David Brodie

Writers
Eric Deeson, Ann Fullick, Andrew Hunt, John Kearsey, Jean McLean, Nicholas Russell, David Sang, Mary Whitehouse

Other contributors
Marilyn Brodie, Moussa Conteh, Peter Galloway, Ralph Hancock, Nigel Heslop, Jane Michell, Michael Moran, Alastair Sandiforth

Project management committee
Lindsey Charles	Heinemann Education
Andrew Hunt	Director
Nicholas Russell	Deputy director
Anthony Tomei	Nuffield Foundation
Linda Westgarth	Administrator

The authors and publishers would like to thank the following people for their generous help with the case studies in this book:

page 4 Sue Russell and Gary Hurst, Farmlab; *page 5* Roger Prutton, Marks and Clerk; *page 5* Earl Dallas and John Hopper, Serck Controls Ltd; *page 6* Hazel Rymer, funded by the Royal Society and working at the Open University; *page 7* Eileen Chadwick; *page 8* Tina Goodman and Sarah Green, Worthing District Health Authority; *page 9* Ena Lynch, SmithKline Beecham Pharmaceuticals; *page 10* Martin Green, SmithKline Beecham Pharmaceuticals; *page 18* Jude Leslie, Alan O'Grady, Jane Taylor and Steve Tandy, Wrexham Maelor Hospital; *page 36* Brian Matthews, West Cranleigh Nurseries; *page 39* Florence Elliot, Moy Park Ltd; *page 44* Samantha Morgan, Matsushita Electric UK Ltd; *page 56* Kate Hollinshead and Max Halliwell, Building Research Establishment; *page 60* Jeff Keenlyside, National Rivers Authority; *page 66* Terry Brinkworth, Claire Oliver, Stuart Dix, Ian Campbell, Julie Gray and Alison Kenyon, SmithKline Beecham Pharmaceuticals; *page 72* Moussa Conteh, Christian Aid; *page 76* Jonathan Tipples, Reed Court Farms, Marden; Laurie Pearson and Joan Davis, Heygate Ltd; and Nigel Pegrum, Pegrum & Sons; *page 80* Claire Dudley, Secrett's Flower Nursery, Milford, Surrey. (Tours of the nursery can be arranged by phoning 0483 426655); and Gill Samways, Woking College; *page 86* Alec Denton, Colin Kenning and Marcus Kendall, Allied Colloids; *page 94* John Ayres, Givaudan-Roure; *page 98* Hugh Barton and Richard Colwill, Scientific Services; and BR Projects Director of Infrastructure; and Dorman Traffic Products Ltd; *page 104* Jenny Page, Special Care Baby Unit, St Richard's Hospital, Chichester; *page 110* Andrew Scotford, RAC Motoring Services, and Graham Harris, Darlaston Community School; *page 116* Michael Clarke, North Derbyshire Tertiary College; *page 122* Kathryn Sandiforth, teacher of Alexander Technique, and Widget Software Ltd; *page 128* Peter Skinner, Johnson Matthey plc; *page 136* Simon Holland, SmithKline Beecham Pharmaceuticals; *page 140* Sister Hilary Holmes and Staff Nurse Julie Lynch, Queens Medical Centre, University Hospital Nottingham, and Kyle Hayes; *page 148* Patsie Stafford-Johnson, Carl Wheatley and Chris O'Reilly, University of Derby.

How to use this book

In your GNVQ course you will be using many different resources, but this book gives you special support. Its chapters match the mandatory GNVQ units and elements, and they contain the information that is required by the GNVQ specification.

These are the components of the book and some hints on how to use them:

Element briefings – at the start of each chapter

The illustrations on these pages quickly give you an idea of what each GNVQ element is about, and the *Targets* and *Key words* tell you what you should achieve. You will find it useful to look at these before starting work on an element and also to refer to them as you go along. When you are preparing for end-of-unit tests you should find that they provide valuable check lists.

Case studies - in every chapter

Case studies are all about people putting science into practice. They are about vocational science. They are more than just stories – they are packed with information and ideas from the GNVQ specification.

Central science boxes – between the case studies in each chapter

This book covers the science that the GNVQ specification requires. It does this partly through *Case studies* and partly through *Central science boxes*. The special point about *Central science boxes* is that they also present the most fundamental scientific concepts in a way that's quick and easy to refer to.

Thoughts and actions – at the end of every chapter

These are questions and activities to help you think about and use the science in the *Case studies* and *Central science boxes*. Some are intended as ideas for assignments, while others will help you to practise core skills in a context of vocational science.

Reference section – at the back of the book

While you work on assignments and on *Thoughts and actions* you might need help with science skills like using graphs, or you might need to look up information such as chemical formulae. You will find such things in the *Reference section*, which has two parts:
- *Techniques* pages help you to learn and use science skills.
- *Data* pages give a selection of the facts and figures you are most likely to need.

Other resources

There is also an Assignment Pack in the Nuffield Science in Practice series. It has over forty ideas for assignments, covering all the mandatory units. It has a *Study guide* which, along with this book, will help you to prepare for end-of-unit tests.

Hazards and safety

Awareness of the hazards and safety is an important part of any scientific work. Many *Case studies* refer to safety matters. There is also a *Central science box* which introduces some general principles of safety laws and regulations at work, and in the *Data* pages you can find more detail. We have provided a warning at the start of *Thoughts and actions* which require practical work.

 Wherever you see this triangle, you should carry out a risk assessment of the practical work and check it and your plans with your supervisor before you begin.

Science at work

Targets for element 1.1

After working through this element you should:

■ have prepared reports on at least two uses of science in services (health and chemical analysis) and two in industries (agriculture, engineering, chemical, pharmaceutical other manufacturing)

■ know how scientific skills can support training, how they are used for research to acquire new knowledge, how they are used to test the nature of materials in chemical analysis, how they are used to develop new products, and how they are used to improve health

■ be able to give examples of science-based work which involve use of equipment (including safety equipment), handling of materials, specific waste disposal procedures, quality control, supervision of people, communication of information. You should have reported in detail on at least three of these

■ know that science-based work is governed by factors which include input costs and output prices and levels of investment

■ know that safety at work is governed by site procedures and regulations, the Health and Safety at Work Act, and in particular by the Electricity at Work Regulations 1989, Control of Substances Hazardous to Health Regulations 1988, Management of Health and Safety at Work Regulations 1992, Personal Protective Equipment at Work Regulations 1993

■ recognise and understand the British Standards Kitemark and the European Standards CE mark

■ know that the commonest hazards at work involve toxic chemicals, high voltages, high temperatures and biological materials.

Key words

Some of the technical words for chapter 1 are listed in the targets. These are some more:
system, consumable, investigation, reference, pharmaceutical, forensic, diagnosis, therapy, monitoring, mean, median, mode, database, sensitivity, reagent.

People working in science

Cross references

All of the case studies in this book, as well as the following Reference pages, will help you achieve these targets:

154 Choosing and using the right instrument

156 Charts, tables and graphs

158 Using graphs

160 Powers of 10

162 Using formulas for calculations

164 Chemical symbols and reactions

169 Statistics

170 SI units and some definitions

180 Conventional symbols in science

182 Health and safety regulations

Targets for element 1.2

After working through this elements you should:

Standard scientific procedures

- have collected and displayed data for at least three tasks, one based on biology, one on chemistry and one on physics. Two of the tasks should be laboratory based and one should be fieldwork based. For one or two tasks you should work on your own and for one or two tasks you should work as part of a team. One of the tasks should involve collection of data over several weeks.
- be able to safely follow standard procedures as described in books and other sources of instructions
- be able to plan the resources needed for each task
- have collected and displayed quantitative data (no numbers) so you can make comparisons or search for patterns
- have collected and displayed quantitative data (with numbers, using statistics, formulas and straight line graphs
- have compared your results with information from computer databases, textbooks, scientific papers and the Reference section of this book
- have written conclusions that are valid
- be able to recognize conclusions that are not valid for particular data
- be able to display data in diagrams, drawings, photographs, bar charts, pie charts, tables and graphs.

Targets for element 1.3

After working through this elements you should:

Adapting procedures to match different needs

- have described an adapted procedure that you have carried out
- have explained the need for adapting the procedure, such as the need for measuring instruments to be more or less sensitive than in the given instructions or the need to use the procedure in a different situation from that in the given instructions
- be able to make changes in the instruments, apparatus and materials used and in the actions performed
- be able to safely carry out the adapted procedure
- be able to evaluate the effects of the changes in the procedure – its success, reliability of measurements, validity of conclusions, how easy it is to do.

Case study: **Science people**

Analysis for sale
Sue Russell and Gary Hurst

Farmlab is a business that analyses animal feed for farmers and feed suppliers. They help people in the agriculture industry to make sure that animal diets contain the right nutrients.

Sue Russell and Gary Hurst are two of the team at Farmlab. Sue is the manager of their labs, which are at Whetstone in Leicestershire. She has a degree in Physiology, Biochemistry and Nutrition of Farm Animals, and she's worked closely with farmers ever since she qualified. Gary left school after finishing his GCSEs and now he's in his early 20s. He's partially sighted, but that doesn't stop him co-ordinating the whole process of testing the samples of feed.

The lab is split into two parts. In the first part conventional wet chemistry goes on, using familiar equipment like test tubes. The second part uses new technology like Near Infrared Reflectance Spectroscopy. The work relies on a close-knit team of dedicated technicians who work with a minimum of supervision. They all know the one basic rule – every sample is processed on the day it comes in.

'We're increasing the information available to farmers about the quality of their home grown feeds,' says Sue. 'It helps them to decide what extra materials to buy in to add to their animals' food.'

Patently obvious *Sue Wright*

'Patent agents like me spend most of their time helping people with applications for patents. A patent is a sort of licence from a government office, the Patent Office, to protect you from other people copying your ideas,' says Sue Wright. 'Clients bring their ideas to me and I turn them into draft patent specifications. That's a description, usually with illustrations, of the structure and purpose of the device and how it works.

I trained in physics and now I specialize in mechanical patents. That means that I work on systems that involve movement, the transfer of force. Anything with pulleys, levers, gears, wheels, springs – things like that. Hydraulics and pneumatics are also very important. Yesterday I was working on a zoom lens for a camera.

We need to know about the law but our training has to be in science, and we learn the law while working in the business. It's easier for a scientist to learn the necessary legal details than it is for a lawyer to learn the science.'

Price, design, production, installation – all under control *Earl Dallas*

Water companies want to be able to find out about water levels, flow rates and so on, and to act on the information using control valves, all from a single control room. They need sensor equipment, cables or microwave links, and a central computer.

Earl Dallas and the rest of his project group at Serck Controls of Coventry are the people who are developing and installing the system. Earl is a Project Engineer, with a degree in Electronic Engineering.

He's involved with the job from beginning to end. He has to work with the company's sales team to help them to work out the price to charge for a particular job. That has to be right – If the company decide to charge a price that's too high then their competitors will get the job. If they set the price too low then they won't be able to make a profit.

'It's the interaction with the customer,' says Earl, 'that makes the job so interesting. We have to find out exactly what they want.' Intensive site surveys are needed before the team work on the details of the system design and prepare a specification for the company's production department to work on.

The job doesn't finish when the parts have been made in the Serck Controls factory. They've all got to be put together and tested on site. Earl takes part at this installation stage, though outside companies come in to do the less technical jobs like fitting cables.

Then there'll be the next job and the next customer. That might be another water company, a power station or a gas distribution network. The company fits systems in Eastern Europe and in the Middle East, as well as the UK. All around the world there's a growing demand for remote control by computer.

High level work *Hazel Rymer*

'One of the good things about studying volcanoes,' says Hazel Rymer, 'is that you have to travel. Most of my expeditions have been to Central America, Iceland and Italy.'

Hazel is a geophysicist working for the Open University. Much of her time is spent at her base in Milton Keynes, but every 12 weeks or so she visits active volcanoes, 'To try to understand what makes them tick,' she says.

'I specialize in taking gravity measurements on active volcanoes,' she explains. 'Small changes in gravity on the surface mean changes in the mass of the volcano. That's the sort of thing that happens before an eruption. The gravity meters I use look like car batteries, but they cost £30 000 each. You have to lug them half way across the world and then carry them up mountains.'

Volcanoes are not friendly places. 'We take hard hats and we're always in radio contact with each other,' says Hazel. 'Sometimes you can't see each other for the fumes that come from the volcano. Everybody has to have a gas mask, and you need tough, old clothes because the acid in the air and on the rock eats through what you're wearing.'

You need all sorts of skills to do Hazel's work. There's a lot of rock climbing to be done and you need to be able to ride horses to reach some volcanoes. But the skills in science are the most important. The expedition has to be well planned, and once Hazel and her team are on the mountain then measuring, checking and recording are what it's all about.

'The first thing we must think about is the scientific purpose of the expedition,' Hazel emphasizes. 'Then we must make sure that we take the right equipment and the right people.'

Once the team and their equipment are on the mountain then the weather might decide what happens first. If it's fine then they must make the most important measurements first, in case the weather changes. Measurements are often repeated several times, and once a few readings have been collected Hazel will spend a few minutes doing some calculations before moving on to another part of the volcano. 'Without all these checks you could get all the way back to the UK and find that one of the instruments wasn't working properly,' explains Hazel.

'Sometimes,' Hazel continues, 'just those few calculations tell us that there's not much going on in that part of the volcano. Maybe the figures are the same as last year's. On the other hand, we might find out that this area is particularly interesting and needs further study. So our plan mustn't be too rigid. We always have to be ready to modify what we're going to do.'

'We write everything down in notebooks at the time. Each book represents thousands of pounds worth of data when you work out the costs of the expeditions. Then when we get back to Milton Keynes we put all the numbers into the computer. The next thing to do is to write up a report.'

Hazel is part of an international network of experts on volcanoes. She doesn't just travel to measure mountains, but sometimes speaks at conferences that could be anywhere in the world. The outcome of her work is that people will become better at predicting when volcanoes are going to erupt.

Food technology *Eileen Chadwick*

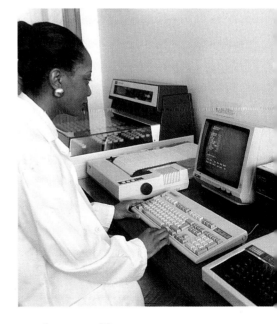

Of course,' says Eileen Chadwick, 'you can mix together a load of approved synthetic chemicals with, say, milk or air, and make something that people can eat. It might be quite nutritious, and it might taste of baked mangoes, but people are more demanding than that. They expect to get the real thing, even in convenience foods. So we have to work out how to add sterile baked mango fragments, keep it tasty and safe, and still have it cheap enough for people to buy and convenient enough for them to prepare during the TV ads.'

Eileen works as a food chemist for a major food manufacturer. Much of her work involves developing foods for large supermarkets. 'We have to keep the delicate flavours and colours stable and keep microbes out. There's so much challenge in this work, and it's exciting when you see something you've created appear in the shops and TV ads.'

'A general science qualification prepares you for an amazingly wide range of careers. My present job could lead me on into more research, marketing, management, or the local authority inspectorate. The only limits are the ones you set for yourself.'

Health promotion
Tina Goodman and Sarah Green

W e try to meet the aims set out in the government White Paper of 1992, *Health of the Nation,*' says Tina Goodman.

Tina Goodman is the Deputy Health Promotion Manager and Sarah Green is the Senior Health Promotion Advisor working as part of the Health Promotion team in West Sussex.

They aim to encourage people to adopt a healthy lifestyle. Surveys of attitudes and habits help them to focus their efforts where they are most needed. For example, the discovery that two-fifths of local people took no exercise was the start of a campaign to get people on the move. They worked with the Leisure Services department training people to carry out fitness testing and with doctors to help them to encourage people to exercise.

Tina and Sarah try to get the messages across in novel and inventive ways. One way is to use the mass media. Some people will accept information from the newspapers more easily than they will from their own local health centres.

'We're also involved in implementing national campaigns in our own area,' says Sarah, 'distributing resouces like videos, posters and leaflets and organizing one-off events like Fun Runs and Health and Fitness shows. It's all a matter of helping people to get more out of life.'

New ways of seeing the world
Abdus Salam

T he Nobel Prizes are not given by any government. They are given, once every year, by an independent organization in Sweden. There is a prize for working for Peace, one for Literature, one for Medicine, one for Chemistry and one for Physics.

The list of winners of the Nobel Prize for Medicine, Chemistry and Physics includes the best known scientists of the last 100 years. The winner of the Physics prize in 1979 was Abdus Salam.

When he won his prize he was not working for a company or for a government but for a university. His research was not intended to develop new products or ways of curing disease. The work had no known applications at all. It was 'pure' research. He was trying to increase what people know about the physical universe. It is possible that, sooner or later, people will find ways of putting his ideas to some use, but that was not why he was doing it.

Abdus Salam is a theoretical physicist. He works on the ideas of physics while other scientists do the experiments. He uses his mathematical skills and his understanding of the laws of physics to create new ways of seeing the world. New ways of seeing the world are bound to seem strange, or even wierd.

The Nobel prize was for showing that the forces of electricity and magnetism could be the same as the forces involved in radioactivity, inside the nuclei of atoms. Abdus Salam went so far as to say that if his ideas were good ones then experimenters should be able to find some strange new particles. People called these particles W and Z bosons, and after a few years experimenters found them by colliding fragments of atoms together. After that it was hard not to be convinced by Abdus Salam's new ideas.

Abdus Salam was born at Jhang Maghiana, Punjab, and though he worked in the UK, he never forgot his roots. He has used his position as one of the world's leading scientists to promote science and education in developing countries. He is the founding President of the Third World Academy of Sciences.

People are depending on you   *Ena Lynch*

'Media Preparation is the beginning and end of everything,' says Ena Lynch, a Laboratory Assistant at pharmaceutical company SmithKline Beecham. Without her, the work of the teams of scientists monitoring drug production or developing new drugs would come to a halt. 'All the glassware comes from us and all the solutions,' she says. 'The diary contains the orders for the week and we have a book with all the Standard Operating Procedures that we need. It tells us what ingredients to use and the order of adding them together. The accuracy of all our balances, pH meters and dispensing machines are checked regularly. Making a mistake can ruin the work of others so you have to get it right. People are depending on you.

COSHH safety rules keep us aware of what we are handling. We get ingredients from the store and for each of them we have full details of any precautions needed and why we have to take them.

I've been here for eleven years and no two weeks are the same. When I was made redundant from a drawing office I couldn't face going back to typing letters for a living. Boredom never plays a part here.'

Planning to keep costs down
Martin Green

Martin Green also works for SmithKline Beecham. He's a Project Group Leader in the Financial Analysis and Planning Department. Over the last 25 years he's had experience in science, work study, accounting, management services and industrial engineering.

For any project within the company he is at the centre of the team who provide an analysis of the cost and feasibility. If a new plant is planned he would be involved in deciding where in the world and on what scale the site would be. He has to develop a cost model in collaboration with the company accountants.

Recently he was involved in the feasibilty study and cost estimates for a £10 000 000 plant at Irvine in Scotland. On a smaller scale he might be involved in the design of a multi-stage process. It's his job to find ways of making things happen at the lowest cost whilst keeping the same high quality. That could mean buying in some materials from other companies whilst making others. Or it could mean changing the technology. He has to explore all the possibilities.

Case study: Science in the news

Reporting results on smoking deaths

SMOKING KILLS 60,000 WOMEN

NEARLY 60,000 British women die from smoking-related illnesses every year – more than anywhere else in Europe.

They are more likely to die from lung cancer than cervical or breast cancer.

British men come third in the European league table of deaths caused by smoking. One-in-three smokers die from

By JILL PALMER

the habit and half of those killed are still in middle age.

The horrifying facts are reported in today's Lancet medical journal which shows that the risks from smoking are far worse than previously believed.

Although the number of male deaths from smoking has dropped from 103,000 to 91,000, the habit is increasing among women, mainly in their teens and early twenties.

More than two million people a year die from smoking in developed countries.

▲ *From* **The Daily Mirror,** *22 May*

There's a lot of science in the newspapers and on TV, like this article from *The Daily Mirror*, and it doesn't take long to see that it's not written in the formal style of a scientific report.

Scientists announce their work in scientific 'papers' that are published in journals that will be read by other scientists. There are thousands of new scientific research reports every week. The scientists who did the work on the smoking deaths published their report in the weekly medical science journal, *The Lancet*. Their original paper ran to ten pages of small type and was one of several reports in that week's issue.

Mortality from tobacco in developed countries: indirect estimation from national vital statistics

RICHARD PETO   ALAN D. LOPEZ   JILLIAN BOREHAM
MICHAEL THUN   CLARK HEATH, JR

Introduction

In countries where cigarette smoking has been common for many decades, tobacco now accounts for a substantial proportion of premature deaths.12 This paper provides estimates for early middle age (35–59), later middle age (60–69), and old age of mortality in developed countries from tobacco during the last few decades of the 20th Cent~~
For one particular country in ~~
method is t~

Materials

Prospective study of a million Americans

The American Cancer Society's second Cancer Prevention Study (ASC CPS-II) is a prospective study of smoking and death among more than one million Americans aged 30 or older when they completed a questionnaire in 1982.[3] In 1992, when the current 6-year results were abstracted, mortality follow-up was virtually complete for the first two years, and about 98–9~~
next four. Because some con~~~
years might h~~

Results

Does the method produce any obviously anomalous results? Only if its results are generally plausible can their implications be explored. Although brief results will be given for 1965 and 1975, chief emphasis will be on the results for 1985 (the last year for which the results are based ~~
actual mortality rates), on approximate extrapol~~~
1995 (the first ~~~~

Discussion

The strengths and weaknesses of the present method of assessing mortality from tobacco in developed countries were discussed as it was introduced and used. The general conclusion was that in such countries it is likely to be reasonably reliable in middle age but somewhat less ~~
at older ages. One simple st~

REFERENCES
1. Zaridze D, Peto R, eds. Tobacco: a major international health hazard. IARC Scientific Publications NO. 74, International Agency for Research on Cancer (IARC), Lyon, 1986.
2. IARC Monographs on the Evolution of the Carcinogenic Risk of

The smoking deaths paper is designed, like most papers, to show that the conclusion is valid because the measurements are reliable. So the writers of the paper devote a lot of space to explaining to other scientists exactly what was done and how. They want to persuade a small group of other scientists, doing similar work, that the work is a real contribution, containing genuine new findings. The paper is not intended to explain things to people who aren't specialists, and so it's hard for us to read.

News reporters and editors are too busy to read every single scientific paper that is published. Even specialist science and medicine reporters cannot look at more than a fraction of the material coming out each week. Yet the smoking deaths story was in every national newspaper, and most TV bulletins, in the UK.

The research was funded by a charity, the Imperial Cancer Research Fund or ICRF. It was the ICRF who succeeded in catching the attention of the journalists. They have a large public relations department, and it's their job to make sure that as many of their medical science stories as possible appear in the media. The reason is simple. Keeping the name of the ICRF in the news is important in helping to raise money from the public for more cancer research.

Margaret Willson is the Public Relations Officer at ICRF. Reporters would soon stop coming to her conferences if the ICRF did not provide good stories. Margaret felt that the publication of this paper was important enough to call a press conference.

◀ *Extracts from the paper on smoking deaths publsihed in* **The Lancet***, 23 May*

At the conference the two senior researchers on the project, Richard Peto and Alan Lopez, spoke about their work, with plenty of visual aids and a handout for the reporters in the form of a press release. This was very different to the original scientific paper – it was trying to communicate with a different audience. It contained a clear summary of the main conclusions of the paper, described as briefly as possible.

The press conference was certainly a success. Margaret was very pleased with the huge amount of press coverage which it received. This was good publicity for ICRF, helping them to continue their work.

▼ *How Margaret Willson told journalists about the research*

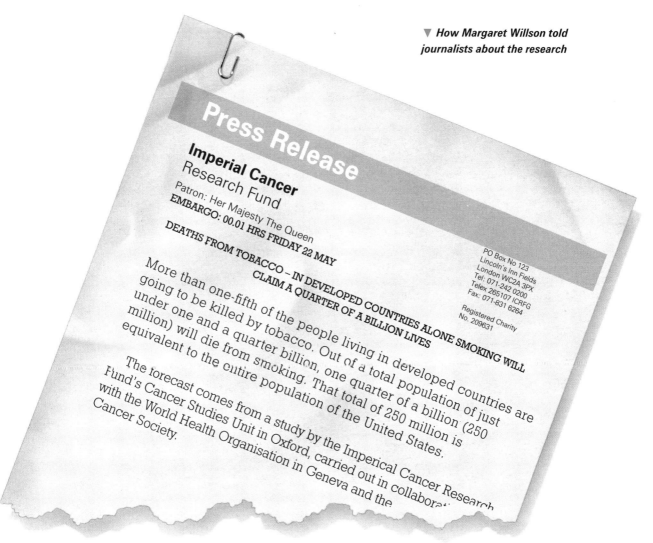

Press Release

Imperial Cancer Research Fund

Patron: Her Majesty The Queen

EMBARGO: 00.01 HRS FRIDAY 22 MAY

DEATHS FROM TOBACCO – IN DEVELOPED COUNTRIES ALONE SMOKING WILL CLAIM A QUARTER OF A BILLION LIVES

PO Box No 123
Lincoln's Inn Fields
London WC2A 3PX
Tel: 071-242 0200
Telex 265107 ICRFG
Fax: 071-831 6264

Registered Charity
No. 209631

More than one-fifth of the people living in developed countries are going to be killed by tobacco. Out of a total population of just under one and a quarter billion, one quarter of a billion (250 million) will die from smoking. That total of 250 million is equivalent to the entire population of the United States.

The forecast comes from a study by the Imperical Cancer Research Fund's Cancer Studies Unit in Oxford, carried out in collaboration with the World Health Organisation in Geneva and the Cancer Society.

Tests and experiments

Observation

It's not possible to get amongst the subject you're working on. You are not in control. All you can do is record what you see.

Watching and recording

Exploration

In an exploratory operation the surgical team set out with an open mind. They don't know what they'll find.

Taking things to bits to see and record what's there

Analysis

When you already have an idea of what is or isn't there you can do specific tests.

Checking out some possibilities

Measurement

You need the right tools and the right procedures to put things into numbers.

Finding out how much

Investigation

If you want to know how one thing affects another you can take control of one of them, one variable, and vary it. Then you watch what happens to the other one. If you're careful, you'll discover the relationship between the two variables.

Controlling variables

Valid conclusions from investigations into relationships between variables

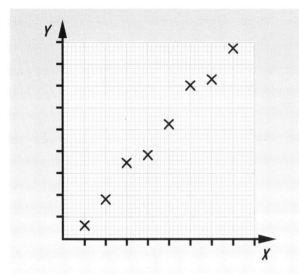

A student has varied variable X and recorded the corresponding values of Y. A pattern emerges that is easy to see on a graph.

It seems that the changes in X cause the changes in Y. But you have to be careful. If there are other variables that are changing then this conclusion is not valid. These other variables could be causing Y to change. You have no way of knowing, unless you make sure that X and Y are the only variables that can possibly change during your experiment.

Is this graph straight or curved? Does it pass through the origin? Before you can reach a valid conclusion you need to know how reliable the results are.

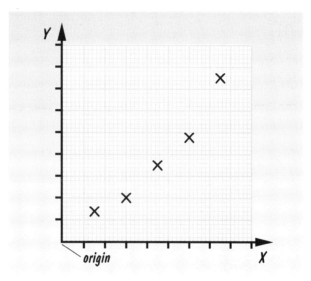

If you know that the measurements are very reliable and there is little possible source of error then you can be quite trustful of the shape that emerges on your graph. But if there are significant possible sources of error then you cannot be so certain until you have collected more results.

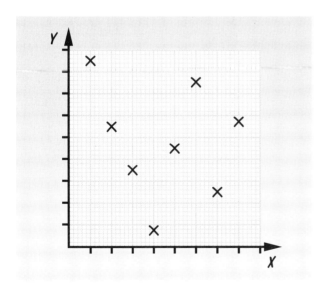

If your results give you a graph like this then the first thing might be to check that the measurements are reliable. Then you can decide on what sort of conclusion you can reach.

In the experiment you have changed X, and Y has also changed. But there is no particular pattern. The only valid conclusion is a very cautious one:

Either:

Y depends on X in a very complicated way and more results are needed to see if any sort of pattern appears,

Or:

Y varies in a way that is independent of X,

Or:

Y could possibly depend upon X but other variables may have also changed during the experiment, and these changes have had enough influence to hide the pattern relating Y to X.

When your results don't allow you to be certain then you should say so.

Safety in the workplace

This worker is wearing an acid resistant PVC boiler suit and a hood over the face with a yoke and a clear viewing space. Rubber gauntlets protect the hands and the boots are acid resistant. The trousers are not tucked inside the boots so that liquid can't run down inside.

In the hustle and bustle of work, where pressures of time and money come up against hazardous materials and equipment, accidents can happen. Every workplace will have its own procedures or regulations, intended to provide maximum protection to the people who work there. As well as that there are national regulations, such as:

▶ Electricity at Work Regulations 1989

▶ Control of Substances Hazardous to Health Regulations 1988

▶ Management of Health and Safety at Work Regulations 1992

▶ Personal Protective Equipment at Work Regulations 1993.

You can find more details of these regulations on pages 182–3.

Pouring acid the safe way

UK law – the Health and Safety at Work Act

The Health and Safety at Work Act (HASAWA) makes every employer have to ensure the safety of all the people who work in the company.

The Act applies to all work premises and activities and to everyone at work – employee, supervisor, manager, director or self-employed.

Health and safety laws are enforced by inspectors who either work for the Health and Safety Executive (e.g. a factory inspector) or for the local authority (usually an environmental health officer). These inspectors may call at any time and talk to any employees, take photographs and even stop work if they consider the conditions are too dangerous. They will also give advice on how to comply with the law.

COSHH – Control of Substances Hazardous to Health

Hazardous substances are used in a wide range of activities, including painting and decorating, farming, laboratories, and printing. Whatever the activity there must be a policy within the business or company on how the risks of using the materials can be reduced.

All hazardous materials must be clearly labelled, both with the name of the material and the nature of the hazard. Suppliers of hazardous materials must also supply a hazard data sheet which describes the substance, outlines the hazards, how it should be stored and how to deal with accidents. Employees using the materials should have access to that information.

Specific site procedures

Specific workplaces need their own specific regulations. This is an extract from a handbook for people who work in laboratories, such as hospital laboratories, where samples of tissue could spread infection.

From *Code of Practice for the Prevention of Infection in Clinical Laboratories and Post-mortem Rooms* (HMSO, 1978)

APPENDIX 2

MODEL RULES FOR LABORATORY RECEPTION STAFF PREVENTION OF INFECTION

1 Wear your laboratory overall, properly fastened, at all times in the reception room and when visiting laboratories. Keep it apart from your outdoor clothing, not in your locker. Pegs are provided.

2 Never wear your laboratory overall in the staff room, canteen or dining room. If you do you may spread infection.

3 Wash your hands often and always before you leave the reception room. Cover cuts and grazes with water-proof dressings.

4 Never eat, drink, smoke or apply cosmetics in the reception room. You may infect yourself. Go to the staff room.

5 Never lick labels.

6 If a leaking or broken specimen arrives do not touch it or any others in the same box or tray. Ask a member of the medical, scientific or technical staff to deal with it.

7 Do not unpack or remove from its plastic bag any specimen with a 'Danger of Infection' label. These are delivered in this way because there is a risk of hepatitis and other diseases. Refer them to a senior member of the laboratory staff.

8 Keep all the specimens together on the reception bench. Never put them on your desk or anywhere else.

9 Twice each day, e.g. before lunch and when you finish work for the day, wash down the specimen bench with the disinfectant and disposable cloths provided.

10 Do not allow visitors to touch anything on the specimen bench. Keep children out of the reception room. They do not know the rules and may become infected.

If you obey these simple rules you will be as safe as anyone else who works in the hospital, BUT if you are ill tell your doctor where you work and ask him to talk to one of the doctors in the laboratory

Case study: **Smooth operations**

▲ *Jude Leslie, Laboratory Business Manager*

Wrexham Maelòr Hospital lies at the foot of the Clwydian mountains of North Wales. At the heart of the hospital are the pathology labs, where samples from hundreds of thousands of people arrive each year. There are samples of blood, samples of solid tissue to be tested for cancer or for infection, samples from cervical smears, saliva, urine – if it's human, they can test it.

Jude Leslie knows the business of a laboratory because she worked in the Haematology department for several years. Now she's the Business Manager, so she's responsible for the annual budget of over £2 million, for staffing and recruitment, for equipment and materials, in fact for making sure that everything runs smoothly. 'My life has changed completely,' she says about her move into laboratory management, and she provides a quick introduction to the size of the business. 'There are a total of 89 people, in four Departments: Haematology, that's blood testing; Bacteriology, identifying bacteria; Biochemistry, chemical analysis; Histology and Cytology, where they can check every sort of human cell.'

The labs provide their services to the hospital and to family doctors. There are plenty of other labs competing to do the same work, so Jude Leslie must make sure that the Maelor labs continue to provide the right quality at the right cost.

Precision procedures under pressure

Specimens of solid tissue arrive in the Histology lab in formalin solution. They could come from an operating theatre where a surgeon needs information about cells from a patient's body. Or they could come from a post-mortem where a pathologist is trying to find out the cause of death of a body. Sometimes a patient will be under anaesthetic on the operating table, and the surgeon needs to know whether a growth in a tissue is cancerous or benign and harmless. That means that Scientific Officer Alan O'Grady has to work under pressure, with complete precision, to make sure that the doctors have what they need to make their decisions and get on with the operation.

(1) Alan O'Grady makes a preliminary inspection of a sample of human tissue that's just arrived from a hospital clinic. Ian Jones takes notes.

(2) Samples in small colour coded cases first have their water removed and are impregnated with alcohol to preserve the tissues.
The next stage is to embed the samples in a block of paraffin wax. The paraffin holds the sample firmly so that it can be thinly sliced.

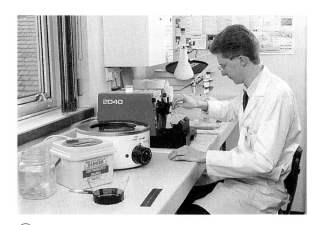

(3) A machine slices the paraffin and the sample into sections just a few micrometres thick. Alan floats the sections that he wants on a water bath so that he can ease it onto a glass slide without damaging it. Waste disposal needs special attention in a medical laboratory – human tissue can carry infection and must be incinerated. Sharp items go into special boxes like the one on the bench.

(4) Quality control – first the sections are stained and then they are checked to see if they are clear enough to help a doctor to make a diagnosis.

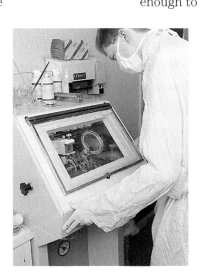

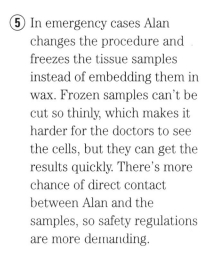

(5) In emergency cases Alan changes the procedure and freezes the tissue samples instead of embedding them in wax. Frozen samples can't be cut so thinly, which makes it harder for the doctors to see the cells, but they can get the results quickly. There's more chance of direct contact between Alan and the samples, so safety regulations are more demanding.

Resource responsibility

Jane Taylor is a Medical Laboratory Assistant in the Bacteriology Department. She makes sure that the Scientific Officers have the materials and equipment that they need so that they can get on efficiently with their work.

'The job I'm doing now is media preparation, making sure that the Scientific Officers have enough plates or Petri dishes, for growing bacteria so they can investigate disease.'

'I went to do a hairdressing apprenticeship but I was bored with that,' she says. 'So when a job came up at a medical laboratory I came here and now I've been here for two years. I've got a lot more responsibility than I ever expected, and I love it.'

'Each day is different. I have to find out what kinds of plate people are going to need and then I do my own schedule for the day. Then at the end of the day I write up how many plates I've made and of the type of nutrient jelly that I've used.'

'It's a very responsible job. If the plates aren't there or they're out of date then it's down to you. Everybody is relying on you so they can do their work. It's enjoyable, though, because you're left to get on with it. And there's a rota, so next month I'll be working on something different.'

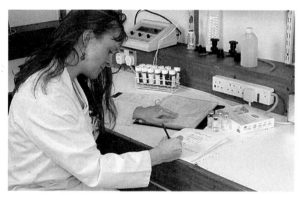

① Record keeping – the start and finish of every job.

② Jane Taylor weighs out the nutrient powder...

③ ...and adds just the right amount of water to get the right concentration.

④ The autoclave keeps the mixture at 121 °C for 15 minutes – enough to kill any bacteria that could interfere with the tests that the Scientific Officers will do later.

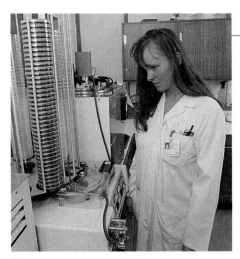

(5) The mixture is just beginning to set into a jelly but it's still liquid enough to be pumped directly from the autoclave into the plates. The machine moves the plates into position and automatically fills each one to the right level.

(6) Once the plates are set they can go into store. Each one will help the Bacteriology team to identify bacteria and disease.

Skill plus safety in the Haematology lab

In the Haematology lab a machine counts and measures the cells in samples of blood. Information technology can quickly provide a display of every test. Scientific Officer Steve Tandy knows what to look for on the computer screen, and he can do more tests on samples that need extra attention.

Further down the lab, Steve and his colleagues make 'blood films' – microscope slides with samples of blood. It's one of those things that looks easy when the experts do it, but it takes skill not to damage the cells, and to get an even spread of the various types of cell across the glass slide. 'Under the microscope we can see whether the blood is normal or not,' explains Steve. 'That's where our experience and expertise come in – detecting subtle differences in shape, size or colour of the cells.' He has to be conscious of the hazards of the work. 'There are dangers of infection from HIV, hepatitis and Weil's disease,' he says. 'That is why we follow strict procedures and everything in the machine is sealed so there's no possibility of human contact with the blood.'

Jude Leslie, Alan O'Grady, Jane Taylor and Steve Tandy are part of a large team who provide answers to doctors' questions about samples from their patients. Every test result must be right. Lives are at stake.

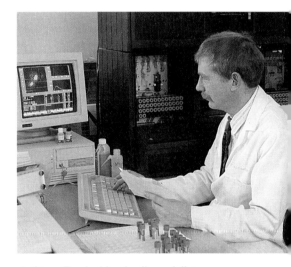

▲ *Steve Tandy, blood cell specialist*

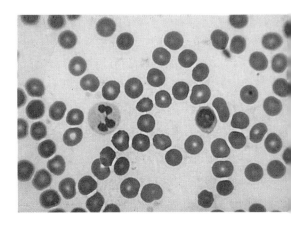

THOUGHTS AND ACTIONS

1 Starting with 'Science people', group the people featured in this book according to the ways in which they use science in their work. Use the following categories:
- science used to support education (including adult education)
- scientific research – obtaining new knowledge and creating new ways of thinking
- scientific analysis – using specific techniques for identification
- science used for development of new products and techniques
- science used to improve health
- others.

2 a For each of the following descriptions of work, choose one person featured in this book whose work fits the description.
- handling materials
- use of safety equipment
- disposal of wastes
- quality control
- supervision of other people
- communication of information
- analysis
- measurement
- investigation
- laboratory work
- field work
- individual work
- team work

b Use the information about these people to create a recruiting poster or leaflet for science courses such as GNVQ Science. You should demonstrate the variety of scientific work that is available to people who follow the course.

3 a Compare the work of Abdus Salam (see 'Science people') with the work of Martin Green.

b Which work would you prefer to do if you had the choice?

c Of all of the jobs featured in 'Science people', which would you prefer to do? Explain why.

4 Read about the work of Earl Dallas on page 5.

a What are the commercial advantages to a water company of installing a central electronic control system?

b Draw a flow-chart to show the various stages of Earl Dallas's work on a major project for a water company.

5 Read about the procedures followed by Alan O'Grady and Jane Taylor in 'Smooth operations'.

a What evidence of record keeping can you find? Why is it important to their work?

b What evidence is there of
(i) measurement   (ii) special safety precautions
(iii) special waste disposal procedures?

6 In 'Smooth operations', Alan O'Grady follows a standard procedure to prepare sections that are just a few µm thick. Sometimes, however, he follows an adapted procedure.

a When might he do this?

b What are the main advantage and disadvantage of the adapted procedure?

7 In the Haematology Laboratory in 'Smooth operations', how does the use of computer and manual techniques lead to efficient work?

8 Look at the 'Safety in the workplace' pages.

a Who has responsibility for inspecting places of work to make sure that they are as safe as possible?

b What powers do they have?

9 Look at the model rules for hospital laboratory reception staff in 'Safety in the workplace'.

a What are the specific hazards in a hospital laboratory?

b Is the list of rules easy to understand and remember?

c Make your own version of the list. You could add illustrations that would make the points on the list easier to remember.

d Read about Hazel Rymer in 'Science people'. Some of the specific safety procedures that she follows are described. Think about others that she might have to follow, and then write a list of 'model rules' for an expedition to a volcano.

10 In 'Science in the news', Richard Peto and Alan Lopez used very different styles of communication in their paper for *The Lancet* and in their press conference.

a Why were the styles so different?

b Their scientific paper in *The Lancet* has a list of 'references'. All papers have a list like this. Why is it important?

11 After reading 'Science in the news' use a computer to prepare a newspaper article, with headline, on the work of Hazel Rymer (pages 6 and 7).

THOUGHTS AND ACTIONS

12 Many research scientists work for universities, and some work directly for charities like the Imperial Cancer Research Fund.

  a How do research scientists tell each other about their work?

  b How do the general public find out about the work of research scientists?

  c Many other scientists work for companies, developing new products and analysing the products of competitor companies. Why would these scientists be less likely to want to explain the detail of their work?

13 A road building company is using a layer of stone 600 mm deep as part of the foundation of a new road. They need to work out how much stone to order. The road will be 10 km long and 8 m wide. Look at pages 162 and 170 in the 'Reference section'.

  a Convert 600 mm and 10 km into metres.

  b Use volume = depth × length × width to calculate the volume of stone that they need.

  c Stone is sold by mass, measured in tonnes. The average density of this stone is 2000 kg m^{-3}
(i) How does this compare with the density of concrete?
(ii) Use density = mass/volume to calculate the mass of the stone in kg.

  d Convert this mass into a measurement in tonnes.

14 Fresho International is a company who develop, make and sell cleaning products. Their leading brands are Fresho, a kitchen cleaner, and Flusho, a toilet cleaner. They also sell Frotho, a cleaner for baths. All three products contain the same fine hard powder which acts as an abrasive – it scratches dirt off surfaces. Unfortunately, Frotho doesn't sell very well because some of the grains of powder are too jagged and they scratch plastic baths.

The company are considering investing £250 000 in developing an improved version of Frotho. They will then have to spend £100 000 on advertising to launch the new product, and extra production costs will make each bottle of the product 3p more expensive than the old Frotho to make.

The company need to get back their investment in development and marketing within two years. They aim to sell 400 000 bottles in the first year and 1 million bottles in the second year. At the moment, Frotho costs 89p per bottle.

  a How will the company find out whether people will pay a higher price for the new product?

  b Suggest what price they should charge.

  c The company decide to investigate the possibility of developing a way of separating the jagged powder grains from the rounded ones. Who will do this work?

  d Create a brand name for the new product and devise an advertising campaign, for example, a slogan, a poster, an outline of a TV ad, which publicizes the scientific work that has gone into developing it. Remember that you might not want to give away the details of the new process to your competitors.

15 Belfast Electronics is a company which has just won a contract to build 400 000 specialist circuit boards for an Italian car manufacturer. They need to build a new assembly line, and they have decided to invest in four robots, instead of employing people, for the repetitive work. Each robot will cost £30 000 and will do the work of one person at a time but will operate for 24 hours each day, so it will replace three people.

However, they will still need a person to work alongside the robots at all times. This person will take over if a robot breaks down, will ensure that the robots have a supply of materials, will perform routine maintenance on the robots, and will be responsible for quality control.

  a How many people will the company need to make sure that there is somebody to work alongside the robots for 24 hours each day?

  b The company's assembly line workers are each paid £10 000 per year for an eight hour shift. How long will it take for the company's savings on wages to equal the cost of the robots?

  c The company decide to retrain one of their existing production line employees to work with the robots. The company has no experts on robots. Who might provide the training?

  d Write a newspaper advert to recruit the other people to work with the robots. The advert should mention the kind of qualifications and experience that are needed. Remember that it is unlikely that the company will find many people who already have experience with robots.

16 At a bakery they need to check their supply of yeast from time to time by measuring its growth rate. These are measurements of the mass of yeast growing in a nutrient solution at a fixed temperature:

Time /min	0	5	10	15	20	25	30	35
Dry mass of yeast/g	1.00	1.06	1.14	1.26	1.41	1.56	1.71	1.82

  a Plot a graph of these results. See page 158 of the 'Reference section' for help in using graphs.
  b What can you say about the rate of growth during the first few minutes, compared with the rate of growth after about 25 minutes?
  c Measure the gradient of the graph for the period from 15 to 30 minutes. What does this gradient tell you about the rate of growth during this time?
  d Repeat this test with yeast, but try it at different temperatures. Work out the ⚠ maximum growth rate in each case.
  e Write a conclusion to this work. See page 15 for help on graphs and valid conclusions.

17 Read about graphs and conclusions on page 15.
A scientist has varied and measured the potential difference (voltage) across a filament lamp and has measured the corresponding current that flows.
  a There are the first results:

Potential difference/V	10	20	30
Current/A	0.10	0.19	0.31

Plot these results onto a graph. What relationship do the results suggest?

  b The scientist continues to increase the voltage:

Potential difference/V	40	50	60
Current/A	0.39	0.46	0.52

Plot these results along with the first set. Describe the relationship between potential difference and cur rent, as far as these results allow.

  c The scientist decides to obtain some more measurements.

Potential difference/V	5	15	25	35	45	55	65
Current/A	0.04	0.15	0.27	0.34	0.43	0.49	0.53

Add these results to your graph. Do they confirm your previous conclusion?

Living things and their environments

Characteristic activities of living things

Responses to changes in the environment

Controlled environments

Targets

After working through this element you should:

■ have prepared a report on one type of living thing that you have studied

■ have monitored the movement, growth and distribution of the living thing

■ have investigated the effects of at least two changes in the environment on the living thing

■ have described an example of human control of an environment in your locality

■ know the different methods that plants, animals and microbes use to obtain energy and nutrients

■ know the different methods by which plants, animals and microbes reproduce and grow

■ know how temperature, light conditions, moisture and grazing by animals influence the growth of plants

■ know how temperature, availability of food and predators influence the movement of animals and their abundance in different places

■ know how temperature and the availability of nutrients influence the growth of colonies of microbes

■ know that people provide controlled environments for living things in the places where they live, e.g. in gardens

■ know that people provide controlled environments for living things for large scale production, e.g. in agriculture and in use of microbes in food manufacture

■ know that the responses of living things can be used to monitor pollution

■ know that people control environments for the sake of nature conservation.

Cross references

Key words

Some of the technical words for this element are listed in the targets. These are some more: glucose, starch, respiration, photosynthesis, waste product, chlorophyll, enzyme, diffusion, decomposers, sexual, asexual, binary fission, fertilization, germination, predator, distribution.

Case study: **Giving nature a helping hand**

▲ *The Cromford Canal in Derbyshire provides a home for many species, thanks to the work of the Amber Valley Groundwork Trust and Jane Michell*

▲ *Jane Michell, environmental consultant, at work on the banks of the Cromford Canal.*

We have all seen bits of countryside or parkland like this canal bank. It is home to many different plants and animals and to countless micro-organisms. Different living things thrive in different conditions. For example, all plants need light to grow, but some plants need more light than others. Some plants grow very tall to reach the light, shading everything below. The only plants that can grow underneath them are the ones that don't need much light. If an environment changes by even a small amount the balance of the organisms which live in it will also change.

People often deliberately change or manage an environment. Farmland and forest, most of our countryside, are environments managed by people for producing food and other useful products. Sometimes people manage environments for nature conservation. This might be to increase the variety of organisms which live there or to protect a particularly rare or threatened species.

Jane Michell is an environmental consultant working in Derbyshire. She investigates the plants and animals in an environment and then uses this knowledge to advise and inform others.

'The Amber Valley Groundwork Trust asked me to write an ecological survey of part of the Cromford canal at Hartshay. I had to survey the existing habitats, assess the wildlife and outline a plan to enhance the wildlife value of the area,' says Jane. 'That meant looking up the results of surveys done in the past, and then getting out into the field. Then I could really find out what the canal banks and water are like, as well as identifying the plants and animals which live there.'

When Jane looked at the canal she found that there were two distinct regions separated by a road. By sampling lots of small areas of both regions Jane could build up a picture of the plants and animals in each environment.

'On this part of the canal bank there is plenty of light allowing grasses to grow. The canal has been dredged and the silt put on the banks. The water can flow easily. There are many stinging nettles growing on the silt taken from the canal. They provide a good food source for certain butterflies.' ▶

◀ 'Brambles, ash, elder and blackthorn form thick cover on these banks. This means little light gets through the cover and the banks themselves are bare. Many insects like dark, wet, muddy places to breed and feed, and these muddy canal banks are ideal. The trees provide homes for insects in their bark and leaves, and nesting sites for a variety of birds.'

The abundance – numbers and types – of ▶
living things in a particular area depends
on the conditions.

◀ A lot of plants like this marsh marigold
need plenty of moisture. Other plants can
survive in dry conditions.

Grazing by animals harms some plants ▶
but enables others to grow.

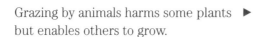

◀ The number and type of small animals
and insects affects the number of
predators in an environment.

◀ Most fish need clean water with plenty of oxygen.

Animals such as these bloodworms can manage in water which is too polluted and low in oxygen for freshwater fish to live in. ▶

When Jane had completed her investigations of the canal banks she suggested ways of managing the canal. 'When I have produced my report it goes back to the people who have asked for it,' says Jane. 'They may have to decide what to do about it, or they may use my report to help them when they are applying for funding from someone else.'

▶ *Part of a report by Jane Michell on the Cromford Canal at Hartshay.*

From: Jane Michell
To: Amber Valley Groundwork Trust

Three possible management options would be:

1 Dredging the canal out to its original banks would open it up and improve the quality of the water – but the heavy dredgers which would be needed to do that would destroy much of the existing banks with their plants and animals.

2 A little minor work pruning some of the existing trees could be done and then the canal left to itself. This would eventually mean the loss of the canal as it would get completely silted up.

3 A compromise between options 1 and 2 – some parts dredged and some left alone. This would provide a pattern of varied habitats with different conditions. As a result there would also be a variety of plant and animals living there, which would be good for conserving the wildlife and learning about the environment.

Photosynthesis and nutrition

Plants have one great advantage over animals – they can make their own food from carbon dioxide and water. They need an energy supply from the Sun to turn these simple molecules into glucose, and the waste product of the reaction is oxygen. The process is photosynthesis and it can be summarized as:

$$\text{carbon dioxide} + \text{water} + \text{energy transfer} \longrightarrow \text{glucose} + \text{oxygen}$$

Chlorophyll is the green pigment that gives plants their colour. They need it for photosynthesis.

Light supplies the energy needed for photosynthesis to take place. It usually comes from the Sun.

Plants take in carbon dioxide with the air through their stomata, small pores in the surface of their leaves. The concentration of carbon dioxide in the air around a plant affects how much it can photosynthesize.

Respiration, which plants, micro-organisms and animals all do, is rather like the reverse of photosynthesis. There are several stages to the process of respiration, but a summary is:

$$\begin{array}{ccc} \text{glucose} & & \text{carbon dioxide} \\ + & \longrightarrow & + \\ \text{oxygen} & & \text{water} + \text{energy transfer} \end{array}$$

Plants give out oxygen as a waste product of photosynthesis. They produce more oxygen than they need for respiration, so plants add oxygen to the atmosphere.

Special proteins called enzymes control photosynthesis. As it gets warmer the enzymes work faster, and so more photosynthesis takes place. But if it gets too hot the enzymes are damaged, and photosynthesis stops.

Plants make glucose by photosynthesis and quickly turn the glucose into starch, which is easier to transport and store. Starch is used as a fuel and as a raw material for new plant tissue.

Water needed for photosynthesis is taken up by the roots of the plant from the soil. Plants also take in small quantities of dissolved elements from the soil. They need these elements for building complex chemicals like chlorophyll.

Nutrient raiders

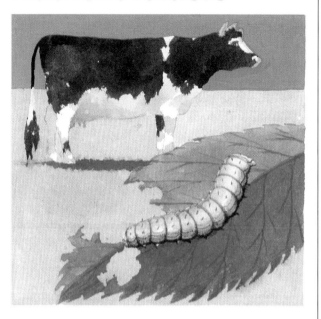

Animals can't photosynthesize but they can respire. Starch and glucose are substances that animals can get from plants, so animals are raiding plants' 'fuel stores' when they eat them.

Animals also need nutrient elements and fats, proteins and vitamins. They get what they need from plants. Sometimes plants just supply the basic chemical building blocks, and the animals build up more complex molecules within their own bodies.

Nutrition and micro-organisms

Some micro-organisms can photosynthesize, like plants do. Other micro-organisms must take in fuel and other nutrients from their surroundings. They give out enzymes which can digest material around them so that it can pass into their cells.

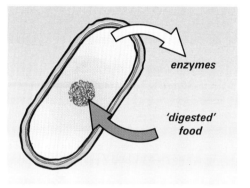

Some bacteria feed by digesting material around them

With underwater plants we can measure photosynthesis by collecting the oxygen they give off.

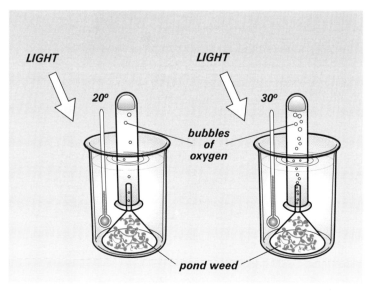

Light and carbon dioxide concentration both affect the rate of photosynthesis.

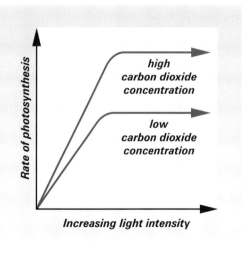

Reproduction and population

Asexual reproduction can happen with just one organism. The offspring are all genetically the same as the single parent.

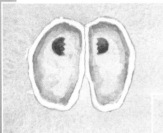

◀ Binary fission – splitting in two – is the simplest sort of asexual reproduction. Many microbes reproduce in this way.

Budding – a ▶ small bud grows out of the parent organism and then separates.
This kind of asexual reproduction takes place in yeast and some simple animals.

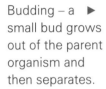

◀ Runners, suckers, rhizomes and stolons are all ways in which plants reproduce asexually.

◀ Bulbs, corms and tubers store starchy food. They help the species to survive underground in winter, after the parent plant has died. The offspring are genetically the same as the parent – this is asexual reproduction.

Cuttings are a form ▶ of artificial asexual reproduction. Small pieces can be cut off plants and they can be encouraged to grow roots.

Sexual reproduction involves two organisms. Often, two specialized cells called gametes meet and join together to create the beginnings of a new organism. The offspring are different from the parents, so that in a whole population of the species there is a lot of variation of characteristics.

Flowers are the sex organs of a plant. The male gamete is carried by the pollen, which travels, with the help of the wind, water, insects or other animals. The female gametes are the ovules that remain in the ovary of the flower where the seeds will develop. Biologists define the male gamete as the one that moves from its parent organism, and the female gamete as the one that stays with its parent organism. The international symbols for male and female (see Reference section page 180) are based on this. ▼

Many types of animal – insects, fish, birds, amphibians and reptiles – produce eggs. Fertilization, the joining of gametes, takes place sometimes inside and sometimes outside the body of the female parent. Birds lay few eggs and take great care of them and of their chicks. Many fish do not care for their offspring at all but instead they lay huge numbers of eggs. ▼

In mammals, the offspring remain protected inside the body of the female parent and receive a lot of care after they are born. Like birds, mammals produce few offspring, but the offspring have a relatively high chance of survival. ▼

Population

▲ Male and female frogs meet and mate in water in the spring. A female frog can produce thousands of eggs (frogspawn). Fertilization takes place in the water after the male releases sperm onto the frogspawn.

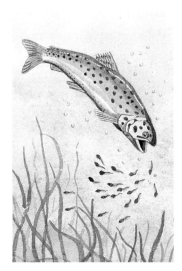

◄ Some eggs may not be fertilized. Even for those that are, the beginning of life is hazardous. The jelly around each egg protects it from predators, but once the tadpoles emerge then they present a valuable source of food to many other animals.

The young frogs that ▶ emerge from the water in the summer must face more predators, disease, possible starvation, and the cold of winter. Very few, perhaps none, of the offspring of the two frogs will survive and return to water to mate in the following spring. If this were not true then the world would have been swamped by frogs, millions of years ago.

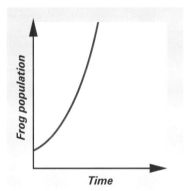

◄ If every frogspawn egg developed and the frog survived until the following spring, then the frog population would rise very rapidly.

Temperature, ▶ availability of food, predators and disease all control the population of frogs. There will be some variation from one year to the next, but the population remains stable.

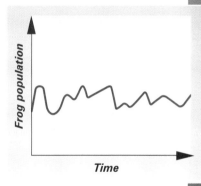

Species that experience rapid growths of population can also experience rapid falls. This can lead to extinction. ▼

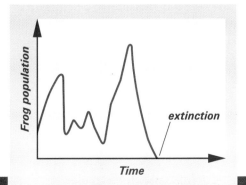

extinction

Bacteria basics

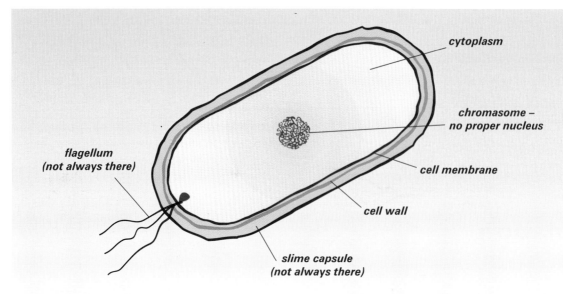

- cytoplasm
- chromasome – no proper nucleus
- cell membrane
- cell wall
- flagellum (not always there)
- slime capsule (not always there)

▶ **Size** Typical bacteria are about 0.0001 mm across. Can only be seen with a light or electron microscope.

▶ **Distribution** Different kinds of bacteria thrive in different conditions. Bacteria can be found anywhere from cold Arctic regions to the water of hot springs.

▶ **Nutrition** Two main types

1 Like animals – some bacteria feed on living animals and plants, others on dead ones. They use enzymes to break the large molecules of food around them into smaller molecules that they can take in.

2 Like plants – some bacteria can make their own food from carbon dioxide and water. Many use sunlight as an energy source, as in plant photosynthesis.

▶ **Reproduction** Mainly asexual – most bacteria simply split in two (binary fission). If they are provided with warmth, moisture and plenty of food they can split in two every 20 minutes. One single bacterium in good conditions can give rise to more than 250 000 bacteria in only six hours.

▶ **Respiration** Bacteria need an energy supply to keep all their chemistry going, just as plants and animals do. So they take in raw materials and they produce waste products. Gases pass easily in and out of bacteria by diffusion. Not all bacteria need oxygen – some are actually poisoned by it.

▶ **Other notes** Some bacteria are very useful, particularly the ones which digest dead plant and animal material. These 'decomposers' put valuable nutrients from the dead plant and animal material back into the soil. They also prevent a build-up of dead bodies. But some bacteria, mainly those which feed on living organisms, cause diseases.

Colonies of bacteria

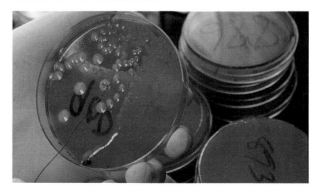

Individual bacteria are so small they can only be seen by using microscopes. But if there are enough bacteria together they can be seen with the naked eye. Colonies growing on agar jelly allow scientists to study the effects of drugs and other chemicals.

Bacteria respond to temperature

We use high temperatures to kill bacteria in food, and low temperatures to slow down their reproduction. But bacteria thrive at the right temperature.

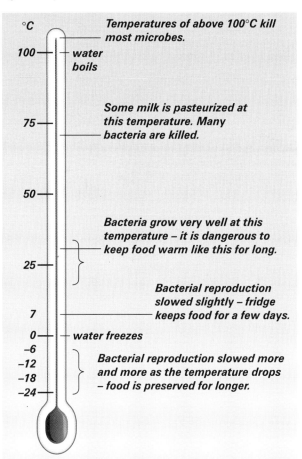

°C

Temperatures of above 100°C kill most microbes.

100 — water boils

Some milk is pasteurized at this temperature. Many bacteria are killed.

75 —

50 —

Bacteria grow very well at this temperature – it is dangerous to keep food warm like this for long.

25 —

Bacterial reproduction slowed slightly – fridge keeps food for a few days.

7

0 — water freezes
–6
–12
–18
–24 —

Bacterial reproduction slowed more and more as the temperature drops – food is preserved for longer.

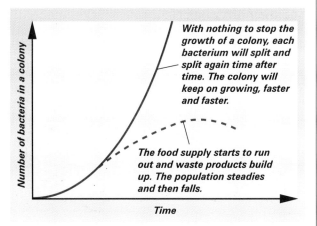

Number of bacteria in a colony

With nothing to stop the growth of a colony, each bacterium will split and split again time after time. The colony will keep on growing, faster and faster.

The food supply starts to run out and waste products build up. The population steadies and then falls.

Time

The rapid rate of growth of a colony of bacteria only lasts a short time. The food supply begins to run out and poisonous waste products build up, so that there is less reproduction or more bacteria die.

Yeasts

Yeasts (microscopic single-celled fungi) are a type of micro-organism. Like bacteria, they are very small, they need warmth, moisture and a good supply of food to grow. But all yeasts feed like animals do. They cannot make their own food. They reproduce asexually but they do not simply split in two like bacteria. Yeast cells form buds which grow and then split from the parent.

When yeast respires with a good oxygen supply it forms carbon dioxide and water, just like plants and animals do. But yeast can also respire for a long time without oxygen, and when it does this the waste products are carbon dioxide and ethanol. The carbon dioxide bubbles make bread rise. Ethanol is the alcohol in drinks, and yeast is a basic ingredient in making beer, wines and spirits.

Viruses

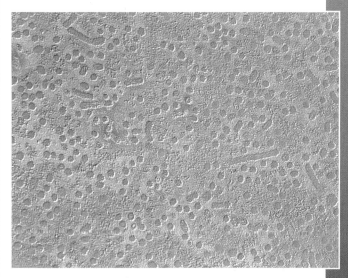

Viruses are much smaller than bacteria or yeast. They can only be seen using an electron microscope and the ones in the photograph have been magnified 95 000 times! Viruses do not feed, respire or grow. They do not have cells and they cannot move themselves about. They all cause disease of one sort or another, for example, 'flu. They do reproduce – but only by taking over the cells of a living plant or animal. They make the host cell use its own chemistry to make many new viruses. Then the cell bursts open and the new viruses are set free to infect more cells.

Case study: Keeping 20 million lettuces under control

There is one giant glasshouse in Sussex that supplies over 20 million lettuces every year to growers in the UK. 'We do everything here, from planting the seed to packing the final product,' says Brian Matthews, who's in charge of quality control. 'It's a highly automated enterprise, with 6 hectares under glass.'

Seeds and germination

▲ The seed pellets come from California. The seed drops through pipes into blocks of compost. The compost from Germany contains the nutrients that are best for early growth.

▲ Brian Matthews in the germination shed where it's dark and damp. After 24 hours in here 99% of the seed will have germinated.

Propagation

A machine lays out the trays under glass for growth of the young seedlings. 'The growing rate of the plants varies with the time of year – just 16 days in the lightest months but in the winter they may need as long as 8 or 10 weeks. Light is just one factor that determines how fast plants grow. Temperature, humidity and CO_2 supply also make a difference and we have to get the balance of these factors right. There's no point in giving extra water or CO_2 to cold plants,' says Brian Matthews.

Overhead pipes in the greenhouse can provide a ▶ spray of mist onto the newly germinated plants, but the humidity is low to discourage fungus. Other pipes carry hot water to provide the heating.

Growing on

The young lettuces are planted either in open fields or in a greenhouse. The white plastic sheeting or 'mulch' keeps water in the soil so that the air above doesn't have to be so humid. It also prevents mud from splashing onto the leaves, and reflects light onto the plants. The extra light can give 15% faster growth.

◄ Brian Matthews inspects the plants for healthy growth. 'We dress the soil with NPK mix (fertilizer containing nitrogen, phosphorus and potassium) and trace elements twice a year,' he says, 'and in the glasshouse we can use the mist spray to apply more NPK if the plants need it. We also have to watch for pests like fungus and insects.'

Climate control

Every 15 seconds, a computer reads sensors which give it information about temperature, humidity, light level, CO_2 concentration, and wind speed and direction. The computer controls the vents, sprays and heaters to achieve the required conditions. It can even telephone the manager at home if something goes wrong in the night.

▲ Operators can instruct the computer to start raising temperature, for example, from 7 °C at 5.00 in the morning to 15 °C by 8.00.

▲ If the weather forecast is for a bright day then the computer can be told to operate the gas burners to supply more CO_2. Instructions to the computer have to include information on the wind so that the right vents are open by the right amount.

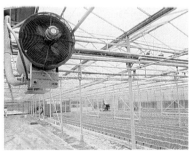

▲ Gas burners heat the greenhouse and produce CO_2 in the process.

Pest control

The robot spray uses the heating pipes as a rail track. It gives uniform and controlled spraying of insecticide and fungicide. 'There are strict limits on when we can spray,' explains Brian. 'We can't use insecticide less than 14 days before harvesting.'

Bio-control, using insects that eat aphids, is an ▶ alternative to chemical sprays for controlling some pests, but customers want 100% insect-free lettuce. Bio-control is better for fruits like tomatoes and peppers where dead aphids on the leaves are not a problem.

Harvest

Machines lift the plastic mulch and that pulls the lettuces out of the ground.

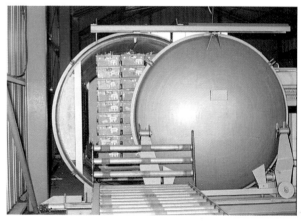

▲ In warm weather the cut lettuces go into a vacuum cooling chamber to make sure they're fresh when they arrive in the shops.

▲ The lettuces are at a convenient height for cutting and wrapping.

Case study: Chicken for dinner

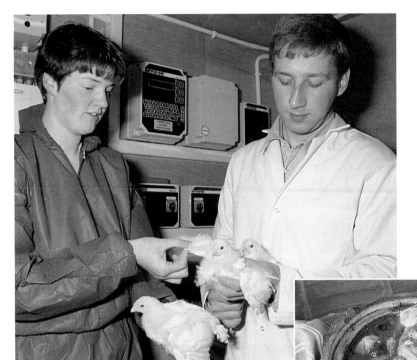

▲ Florence Elliott advises farmers on growing healthy chickens

▼ Chicken meat supplies protein to a lot of people

In the UK we eat an enormous number of chickens – in Northern Ireland alone around 3 million chickens are sold each week in butchers' shops and supermarkets. To produce that number of birds of the right size and weight at the right time takes an industrial process with a difference. Moy Park Ltd is a company based at Craigavon in County Armagh. They control production at 160 'broiler' farms throughout Northern Ireland. Broilers are chickens which are specially bred to be eaten rather than to lay eggs.

Careful breeding has resulted in broiler chickens that have the right characteristics. They grow quickly, from hatching to the dinner plate in around six weeks, converting their feed into meat with as little 'waste' as possible. Their meat is a colour that people like, and they are resistant to disease.

Moy Park Ltd buy day-old 'grandparent' chicks from a breeding company in Scotland. Each year, 70 000 of these female birds are mated with cockerels to produce 9 million eggs. These eggs hatch and the new generation of hens mate. It is their offspring that are the actual broiler chicks.

Florence Elliott from County Fermanagh is 24 and is one of a team of 'broiler advisors' who visit all of the broiler farms regularly to make sure there are no problems. After completing a degree at Sheffield University and an HNC in Agricultural Marketing Florence joined Moy Park Ltd.

'One of my first tasks was to spend a few months as a grower, raising the birds myself,' says Florence. 'After that I really knew the practical problems of the job – and so I was ready to join the advisory team.'

Florence is responsible for 24 farms and visits each one twice a week. Broiler chickens are reared in special broiler houses which have been designed both to look after the welfare of the chickens and to make their care as easy as possible.

Florence has to 'scrub up' before she enters a broiler house. Chicken diseases are rare in Northern Ireland but great care is taken to make sure that infection does not enter the broiler houses from the outside world.

'When I visit a broiler house I have a whole series of checks to make,' says Florence, 'and one of the most important things is simply to observe the birds themselves. The way they look and behave tells me a lot about the overall situation in the house. For example, if there is a draught, or the lighting is uneven then the birds tend to be unevenly spread around the house'

There are about 20 000 chickens in the average broiler house. Department of Agriculture regulations mean that there must be between 12 and 18 birds per square metre, depending on the size of the birds.

An alarm is fitted to show when conditions in the house change for the worse, so action can be taken before the birds suffer.

Good ventilation is vital – it gets rid of moisture produced by the birds, gets rid of the smell from the droppings and helps with temperature control.

The feeders are automatic – they supply the correct amount of food for the age and size of the birds.

Gas-fuelled heaters keep the house at the right temperature. It needs to be quite warm, about 30 °C for the day-old chicks, but the temperature can be dropped to around 22 °C by the time they are four weeks old.

Poultry need a lot of water and do not thrive if there is not enough to drink. The water system is metered so the amount the birds are using can be checked daily.

The floor is covered with chopped straw known as litter and Florence takes samples of this regularly to test for signs of disease.

There is an emergency generator in case of power cuts, so that the environment in the houses can be kept the same.

A broiler house is designed to give the chickens a good environment for growth. The temperature, amounts of food and water and light levels are carefully monitored to make sure that the chickens are ready for the supermarkets as soon as possible.

Between each batch of birds the broiler houses are carefully cleaned and disinfected. The birds enter the house as day-old chicks – and leave for slaughter just 42 days later. Males and females are kept in separate houses. They are fed carefully balanced food that is very high in protein for growth to begin with, but has less protein and more carbohydrate at the end of the process.

The growth of the chickens – both their food intake and their weight gain – is very carefully monitored by the growers. This is to make sure that conditions are right and the birds are gaining weight as quickly as possible.

Broiler chickens are part of a living production line – but is it fair to the animals?

'If an intensive broiler system is properly managed it is most humane,' comments Florence Elliott. 'The birds can be checked regularly, they have constant food and water and the climate is controlled to give comfortable conditions all the time.'

GROWER'S RECORD

Grower	J. Moran
Farm	Mourne Lane
Date	17 May

Standards

Age/days	Males/g	Females/g	Actual/g
1	36	36	–
7	141	136	136
14	404	681	409
21	790	1044	795
28	1180	1407	1203
35	1634	1816	1657
42	1998	–	2225

Amount of feed per 20 000 birds   21.00   tonnes

1 Willow, marsh marigold, stinging nettle and grass are all plants that grow on a canal bank, such as the one featured in 'Giving nature a helping hand'.
   a Which of these needs very moist soil?
   b Which will keep on growing despite continuous grazing by animals?
   c Why do you think that stinging nettles are the dominant species growing on silt from the canal?

2 Jane Michell presented the Amber Valley Groundwork Trust with three options for the canal bank at Hartshay. Which option do you prefer? Say why.

3 Choose two different areas of about the same size, such as gardens, parks, or woodland, and carry out environmental surveys. Use suitable books to help you to identify plants and animals. Draw plans of the types of plants growing and note down any animals – particular birds, insects, worms, etc. – that you find.

   Make a table to show the similarities and differences between the two areas. Try to explain your observations in terms of the environment – soil, light, drainage, – and the uses to which it is put. What effect do people have? How do the plants affect the types of animal that are found there?

4 Compare the way the environments are controlled for growing lettuces in 'Keeping 20 million lettuces under control' and for growing flowers in 'Some Sectretts of success' in chapter 3.1. Make a list of the similarities.

5 Write a specification for a computer program to monitor and control the environment in a greenhouse used for growing lettuces.

6 Read 'Chicken for dinner'.
   a Use the Grower's record to plot a graph of the growth rate of the grower's broiler chickens. Plot age on the x-axis and mass on the y-axis.
   b The 'standards' are the expected growth rates. Plot these on the same axes as in (a) and use the graph to decide whether the grower's chickens were male or female.
   c What is the average growth rate over the six weeks?
   d By how many times is a six-week-old chick heavier than a newly hatched chick?

   e A new-born human baby has a mass of about 3500 g. If a human baby increased its mass by the same factor as a chick during its first six weeks, what would its mass then be? How does this compare with your own mass?
   f What is the mass of a six-week-old broiler chicken to the nearest kg?
   g What is the mass of food consumed by each bird over its six-week lifetime?
   h How can the mass of the bird be bigger than the mass of food it eats?
   i If a broiler house contains 20 000 birds each of the mass calculated in part (f), what is the total mass of chicken, in tonnes?
   j What is the value of all these birds at an average price of £1 per kg?

7 Some people say that animals should not be bred and reared for meat. Produce a poster or leaflet,

   either, for use by a meat producers' association to convince people that rearing animals for meat is humane and acceptable,

   or, for use by animal activists to convince people that the production of meat is inhumane and wasteful and that vegetarianism is a better option.

8 Plants, animals and micro-organisms all need small quantities of the element phosphorus in their bodies.
   a What do plants need it for?
   b Where do plants get it from?
   c How do animals obtain phosphorus?
   d How can micro-organisms obtain it?

9 Read about a use of micro-organisms in 'The right material makes powerful medicine' in chapter 2.3.
   a What types of micro-organism are being used?
   b How does the drugs company control the conditions in which the micro-organisms are living and reproducing?

10 a A single bacterium settles in a warm place with a good supply of nutrients, and a colony develops. Plot a graph to work out the size of the population of the colony after 3 hours if every bacterium were to split in two every 20 minutes.
   b Why does the population not go on rising in this way?

Materials, properties and uses

Measuring properties

Matching properties to uses

Relating properties to structures

Hazards and safety

Targets

After working on this element you should:

■ have prepared reports on the properties of a metal, a ceramic, a polymer and a composite to show your achievement of the targets

■ have carried out experiments on the properties of at least three different materials and have prepared accounts of how the properties of the materials are related to their particle structures

■ be able to follow set procedures to measure density of materials

■ be able to make measurements to compare properties of tensile strength (breaking force), relative hardness, stiffness, electrical resistance and thermal conduction of materials

■ understand the importance of these properties in the choice of materials in buildings and in items of equipment

■ understand the importance of brittleness, transparency and melting point in choice of materials in buildings and in items of equipment

■ understand that materials are made from individual identical atoms or from molecules or from giant structures

■ know that giant structures are arrays of very large numbers of atoms, and that they can result in crystalline or amorphous solids

■ know that polymers are solids with large molecules which have repeating patterns of atoms

■ know that composites are materials made of mixed solids, which have very different properties

■ know that materials are held together by attractive forces or bonds between atoms, and that these bonds are called either 'ionic', 'covalent' or 'metallic'

■ understand the role of electrons in bonding between atoms

■ know that bonding between molecules is usually weak.

Cross references

The following pages in this book will also help you to achieve these targets:

62 Compounds and ions

154 Choosing and using the right instrument

156 Charts, tables and graphs

158 Using graphs

160 Powers of 10

162 Using formulas for calculations

170 SI units and some definitions

172 Properties of substances

Key words

Some of the technical words for this element are listed in the targets. These are some more: force, tension, newton (N), cross-sectional area, current, amp (A), voltage, volt (V), resistance, ohm (Ω), mass, volume, strong and weak, stiff and flexible, hard and soft, brittle and tough, transparent and opaque, electrical conductivity, thermal conductivity, ion.

Case study: Tube technology

▶ *At the MELUK factory in Cardiff they make Panasonic TVs for the whole of the European market. The circuit board map shows their various sales bases in Europe.*

▲ *It takes dozens of different raw materials to make a television. Most of them come out of the ground, like oil and metal ores. TV makers have to know how materials behave.*

▲ *Computer aided design of Panasonic TVs – putting the right materials together*

Materials under extremes of stress

1 **No material at all except for a beam of electrons shooting through a vacuum**
The high-speed electrons hit the screen and make it give out light.

2 **Thick glass tube**
There is a high vacuum inside the tube. The outside pressure results in large forces acting on the tube. But glass is brittle so it must be very thick, and that makes TVs heavy.

3 **Dense 'high lead' glass**
When fast electrons hit a TV screen they lose a lot of energy. The screen gives out visible light and also some X-rays. The X-rays could be harmful so the glass at the front of the screen has more lead than usual to act as an X-ray filter. The lead gives the glass a high density.

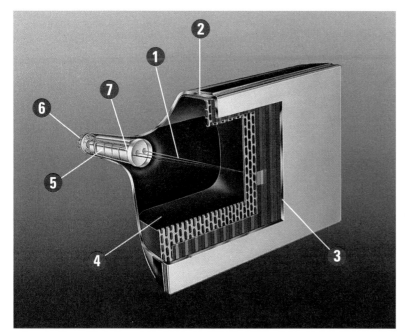

▲ *The heart of a TV is a cathode ray tube. High temperature, high vacuum and high voltage all put materials under stress.*

4 **Thin metal film**
Electrons bombarding the screen can't flow through glass. Electrons could build up on the inside of the screen and they could repel the electrons still arriving in the beam. That would distort the picture. So a very thin layer of metal conducts the electrons away from the screen.

5 **Metal to shield the glass from sudden temperature changes**
Metal wires inside the electron gun have to be hot so that they can provide a supply of free electrons. Glass is a bad thermal conductor so when the TV is switched on the inside of the glass, close to the electron gun, could heat up quickly and expand. The outside will take longer to heat up and expand. Glass is a brittle substance, and it can crack due to this difference in expansion.

7 **Metal inside the electron gun**
Some of the electrons in metal crystals are free to wander between the atoms. If the metal is hot then a lot of electrons escape completely from the metal into the surrounding space. Hot metal at the back of the electron gun provides a supply of escaped electrons. Then a high voltage accelerates them towards the screen.

6 **Plastic insulators**
The atoms in the molecules of plastics are not close enough together for electrons to pass from one to another. So plastics make good electrical insulators.

High on features, low on price

'The so-called cathode-ray tube is a complex beast,' said Manjit, an engineer at Panasonic. 'It's a specially shaped glass mushroom with a high vacuum and some precision electrical components inside.'

'TV set design isn't static. There's constant development by our own research teams, and our customers expect better and better sets every year. So we can't relax. People want improved colour and sound, teletext systems and larger screens. We're developing digital features like slow-motion replay and windows showing other channels. And it all has to be at the lowest possible selling price.'

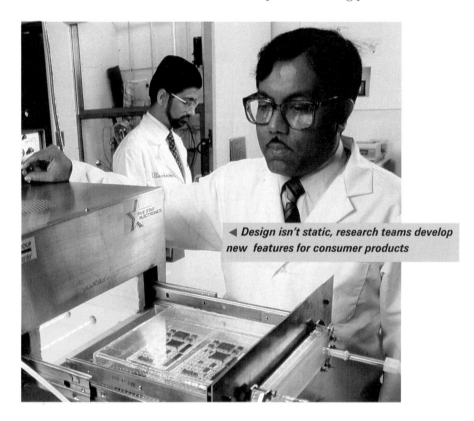

◀ *Design isn't static, research teams develop new features for consumer products*

Case study: Reincarnation

▶ *Can they live again?*
The problem with recycling
cars is that they contain many
different materials all carefully
assembled together

CARS DON'T live for ever. Sooner or later they are scrapped, and usually dumped in a rusty graveyard. Chemical attack to their metal parts is the most common cause of death. But now some car makers are trying to build cars that can be reborn as shiny new models.

Recycling is a beautiful idea. It cuts down on the demands we make for raw materials from the Earth – materials such as copper, iron and oil. It also cuts down on the energy needed to make a car – if iron is already separated from its ore then you don't have to use a high energy blast furnace to do it again.

The main difficulty in recycling most car parts is that they are made of several kinds of material. The cost of separating the different materials is often more than their scrap value. So car makers are now designing cars that will be easy to dismantle. They are making sure that recycling makes environmental *and* economic sense.

1 **Metal** Steel body shell: can be crushed and melted down.

2 **Metal** Engine: cast iron or aluminium alloy cylinder block. There are also steel bolts, bits of steel sheet, and bronze bearings. There's enough metal to make it worthwhile to separate the parts, but it takes time.

3 **Metal** Gearbox: mostly steel and no problem to recycle.

4 **Metal** Wheels: steel wheels and alloy wheels are easy to recycle.

5 **Metal, polymers and other materials** Electrical circuits: may contain valuable materials – some micro-processors have gold connectors. But there will be other materials, like plastic circuit boards, and most things are too small to dismantle to make recycling economically worthwhile.

6 **Polymer and metal** Tyres: rubber, nylon or rayon cord and steel wire firmly bonded together. One of the most difficult recycling problems.

7 **Polymer and metal** Steering wheel and other controls: they have to be designed with as few different materials as possible if they are to be recycled.

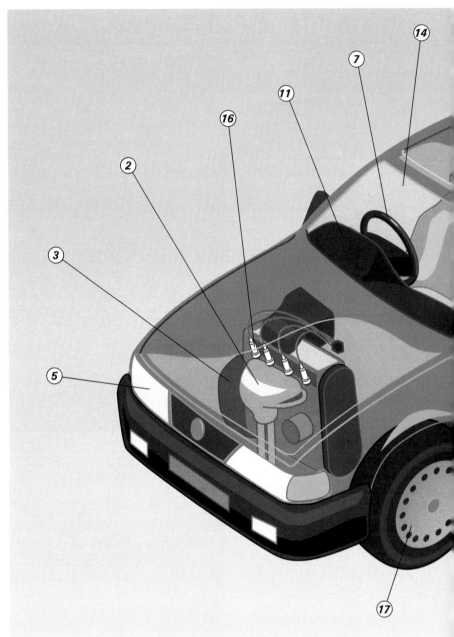

8 **Polymer and metal** Seats: steel tube frames criss-crossed with rubber webbing, with polyurethane foam blocks covered with nylon or PVC-coated fabric. They have to be easy to dismantle.

9 **Polymer** Rubber window and door trim: can be melted down but often contains metal stiffening which makes this more difficult.

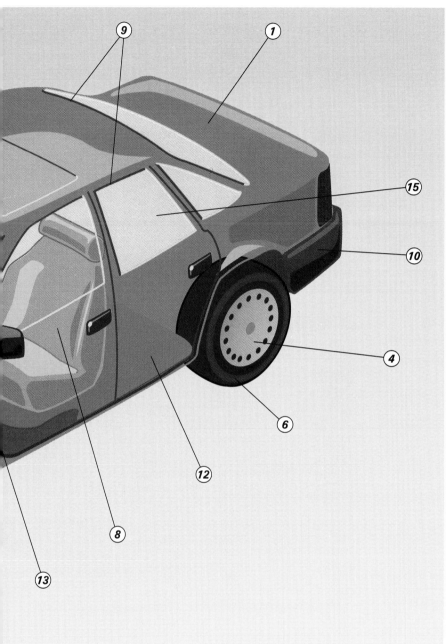

14 **Glass and polymer**
Windscreen: laminated
(layered) safety glass, with a
glass–plastic–glass sandwich.
Can't be economically melted
down but can be used to make
'glassphalt' which is a mixture
of crushed glass and asphalt
that makes a very hard-
wearing road surface.

15 **Glass** Side and rear
windows: toughened glass
that can be melted down, but
if the windows are broken
while still in place it's not
worth picking up the small
fragments.

16 **Ceramic** Spark plugs and
some other engine parts:
ceramic materials are ideal as
insulator material in spark
plugs. They withstand the
high temperatures in the heart
of the engine without melting
or corroding. But it isn't
worth dismantling a spark
plug for the sake of a small
quantity of ceramic.

17 **Composite** Composite
materials are hard to reclaim
because they are mixtures of
materials that are hard to
separate. They are also
difficult to reshape. Car brake
pads are made from
composite material, but used
pads are not worth saving.

10 **Polymer** Bumpers: strong
plastic – only new plastic will
do to make these, but they can
be recycled to make parts that
don't have to be so strong.

11 **Polymer** Grille and dashboard:
can be made of recycled plastic.

12 **Polymer** Carpets and fabric
trim: usually nylon, which can
be melted down.

13 **Polymer** Sound insulation
under carpets and behind
panels: can be made of very low
grade plastic which has already
been used and recycled several
times

Material properties

Tensile breaking force – it's important in food packaging

Tensile breaking force of a piece of material, like this crunchie bar wrapper, is the stretching force that's needed to break it. If you want to make a comparison of the strength of different materials you have to make sure that all your samples have the same cross-sectional area.

Archeologists measure the electrical resistance of the ground to help them find ancient buried ruins

A sample of material with low resistance will allow a large current to flow through it, compared to the voltage that's applied to it.

How to keep the inside warm when the outside is cold

Energy transfer is slow when thermal conductivity is low. To measure thermal conductivity you first have to measure the rate of energy transfer through the material, such as the quilt in this picture. Then for reliable comparisons of materials you must do all your tests with equal conditions – the same thickness and cross-sectional area of material, and the same difference in temperature between one side of the material and the other.

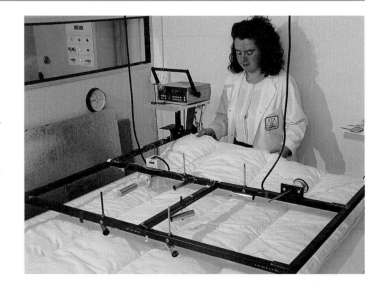

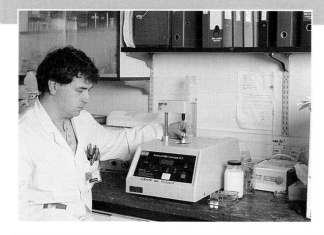

Melting point – a useful fingerprint of a material

Most materials melt at a very definite temperature. Measuring the melting point can be enough to identify a material.

24 carats – pure gold, with a density of $18.9\,g\,cm^{-3}$

People make alloys of gold to make cheaper jewellery. Most other metals are less dense than gold, so if you find that your 'gold' ring has a density less then $18.9\,g\,cm^{-3}$ then your ring is less than 24 carats.

Diamond is hard to cut – a hard material

Diamond is a very hard material, resistant to scratching. Other materials can't scratch it, but it can scratch and cut them. You can make a list of the relative hardness of materials by seeing which ones will scratch others.

Scared stiff?

Rope is not a stiff material, but it's stiffer than rubber. It doesn't bend or stretch so easily. Rope would kill the bungee jumper, but rubber is flexible enough to gently slow him/her down. Using a material with the right properties is a matter of life and death.

Alternative models for understanding atoms

It's only recently that people have managed to produce direct images of individual atoms. Each spot on this picture is produced by a single atom. But we still have to use our imaginations when we're trying to understand the atomic microworld. The pictures we build in our minds, and on these pages, are called models. Models represent the real thing, but they are not the real thing.

We can use various different models to help us to think about how atoms behave. Scientists do this all of the time – they use different models of the same thing to help them solve different problems. The two central pictures on these pages show two different models. They can both be useful.

Simple ball model

Atoms really aren't this simple. But when we're thinking about how large numbers of atoms are arranged in materials there's no point in drawing complicated pictures. The simple ball model works well.

Gas – neon

A simple ball model of a gas like neon is good enough to provide a picture of how gases exert pressure. It's just a matter of a large number of high-speed collisions with surfaces around the gas.

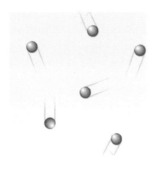

Liquid – water

In water the atoms are not all the same – there are hydrogen and oxygen atoms grouped together in molecules. There's a lot of movement, a dynamic jostling and mingling of particles.

Solid – sodium chloride

This represents sodium and chlorine in a crystal of sodium chloride or common salt. There are electric forces of attraction holding the crystal together. We say that the atoms of sodium and chlorine now have positive or negative electric charge. They are now ions.

This is another way of showing the arrangement of ions of sodium and chlorine in a salt crystal. The ions are shown quite small but the sticks emphasize their orderly arrangement.

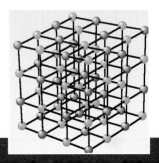

The chemistry of the human body, and the chemistry of drugs, is about the interactions of atoms in large molecules. Glaxo is a drugs company that hopes to get ahead of its competitors by using virtual reality to help their scientists get a new feel for the structure of complex molecules.

Virtual reality atoms and molecules at Glaxo

Electrons and nucleus model

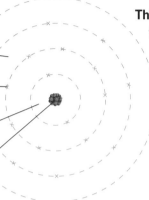

empty space

electrons, in orbit in layers or levels

the positive charge in the nucleus balances the negative charge of the twenty electrons in this atom

the nucleus of the atom

This model shows more detail and it's helpful for thinking about the electric forces that attract electrons to the nucleus of an atom. This atom is electrically neutral. Everything to do with the structure of materials and with reactions between materials depends on the electrical behaviour of atoms.

Ionization

Ionization is about upsetting the electrical balance of an atom. To picture how it happens we have to use this more detailed atomic model. If an atom gains one or more electrons then it has more negative charge – it becomes a negative ion. If it loses one or more electrons it becomes a positive ion.

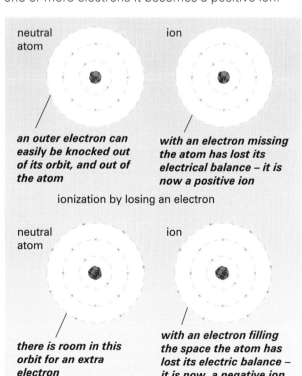

neutral atom

ion

an outer electron can easily be knocked out of its orbit, and out of the atom

with an electron missing the atom has lost its electrical balance – it is now a positive ion

ionization by losing an electron

neutral atom

ion

there is room in this orbit for an extra electron

with an electron filling the space the atom has lost its electric balance – it is now a negative ion

ionization by gaining an electron

Electric current in metals

An electric current is a flow of electrically charged particles, like electrons. In metals the atoms are very close together and electrons can move freely from atom to atom.

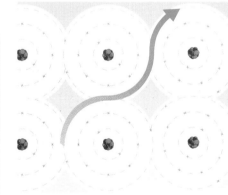

some electrons can flow freely through an array of closely packed metal atoms

Another model

It is more accurate to show the electrons in fuzzy clouds rather than in neat orbits. But this diagram is more difficult to draw and it's harder to see how many electrons are in each layer or level. Being more accurate doesn't always make it more useful.

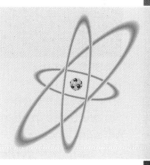

Structures and properties

What do we mean by particles?

Atoms - the building blocks of all materials.

Molecules - groups of atoms that make up some materials.

Ions - atoms or groups of atoms with electric 'charge'.

Electrons - electrically active units from inside atoms. We describe them as having 'negative charge'.

LIQUIDS – molecules are sorted according to their size at an oil refinery

Crude oil is a mixture of molecules of different sizes, made with hydrogen and carbon. The molecules can easily slide past each other. Different sized molecules boil at different temperatures. Oil refineries take advantage of this to separate out different liquids like hexane and octane.

crude o

GASES – methane burning

Most gases are made of molecules, not individual atoms. These methane molecules each have two different kinds of atoms, carbon (black) and hydrogen (white). The molecules move at high speed and they exert little force on each other.

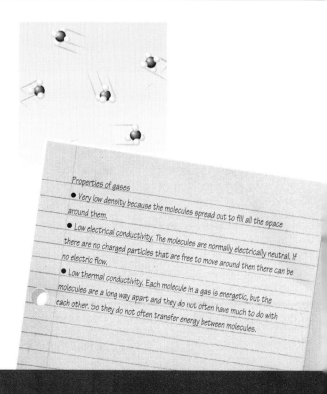

Properties of gases
- Very low density because the molecules spread out to fill all the space around them.
- Low electrical conductivity. The molecules are normally electrically neutral. If there are no charged particles that are free to move around then there can be no electric flow.
- Low thermal conductivity. Each molecule in a gas is energetic, but the molecules are a long way apart and they do not often have much to do with each other. So they do not often transfer energy between molecules.

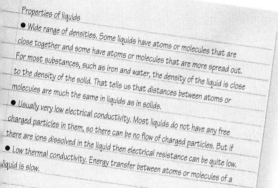

hexane   octane

This represents polythene, which is a tangle of very long 'chain' molecules. Polythene is soft and fairly tough.

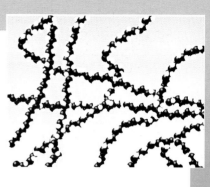

Metals have giant crystal structures and layers of atoms can slide over each other so it's possible to stretch and bend metals. Some metals are harder than others, though most of them are tough.

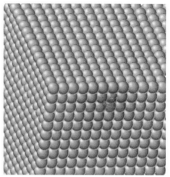

Glass might be transparent, like a diamond, but the two materials are very different. This model of glass shows that it doesn't have a regular crystal structure but the atoms and their bonds make almost random shapes – glass is called an amorphous material. Glass is hard and brittle.

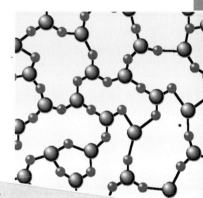

SOLIDS – materials with varied structures amongst their atoms, and with different uses in human-scale structures

Case study: **Concrete results**

▲ *Kate Hollinshead –*
setting European
standards

KATE HOLLINSHEAD and Max Halliwell help to set concrete standards for the European building industry. They work on ways to protect and strengthen concrete at the Building Research Establishment in Hertfordshire.

Like other ceramic materials, concrete is strong when it's compressed – it doesn't easily crumble, even when there is a very large load on top of it. That's what makes it such a good building material. But concrete on its own is not strong when it's under tension. It cracks easily. Steel reinforcement increases the tensile strength.

Reinforced concrete is a composite material. It combines the relatively low expense and convenience of concrete with the high tensile strength of steel. Unfortunately, steel suffers from chemical attack – it corrodes. That's what Kate Hollinshead works on.

Kate Hollinshead is working on a project looking at the repair of steel reinforced concrete structures where the steel is corroded. Her work will establish repair standards for the whole of Europe. People will be able to look up information about repair materials to decide what to use in any particular situation. Kate explains.

'We're trying to find out what are the most important properties that repair materials should have. Do repairs have to bear any structural load? How important is the bond between the repair and the original concrete? That's the kind of question we're asking.

First of all we've looked at a range of bridges and other structures that have been repaired. But the trouble with looking at old repairs is that the quality of the work varies and it's impossible to make a complete assessment. So we're also doing 'natural exposure tests'.

We take specimens of damaged concrete and repair them. We expose them to the elements – in sea water, in spray and on the motorway. Then we look for cracks that might be signs of corrosion in the steel reinforcement, and we look for shrinkage. We connect a voltmeter to the steel in the concrete and to the concrete itself. A high voltage means a high rate of corrosion of the steel.

Finally, we're doing accelerated tests. We try to speed everything up. We spray salt on the samples because that affects the rate of corrosion. We heat them and cool them. We try increasing the concentration of carbon dioxide in the air around the concrete. Concrete is very alkaline and that's what protects the steel, but carbon dioxide reacts with the calcium hydroxide in the concrete. That reduces the pH and corrosion is faster.

At the end of all this we should be able to say what the really important properties of the repair material are. We might recommend exactly what kind of anti-corrosion protection people should give to the steel in harsh environments. For example, some steels have a special coating of resin. We could recommend that people should use stainless steel in certain structures. But coated steel and stainless steel are very expensive, so it's important that we get our recommendations right.'

▼ *Max Halliwell using X-rays to examine crystal structure*

Measuring tensile strength

Max Halliwell left school at 16 and got a job in an insurance office. Then he got a job at the Building Research Establishment and they gave him support to study. They even paid for him to go to university to study chemistry. Now he tests the properties of concrete that's been attacked by sulphate ions. He's trying to discover how different kinds of concrete might be most suitable in different building conditions.

'We immerse concrete in sulphate solution,' explains Max. Then we work with several variables and find out how long it takes to see the effects. We use different strengths of sulphate solution, for example, or we vary the temperature. We measure tensile and compressive strength by testing the samples to destruction. Using X-rays helps us to examine the crystal structure of our samples.'

Steel is not the only material that can be used as reinforcement. At the Building Research Establishment they've studied a whole range of cement-based composite materials. They've used natural fibres like sisal as well as polypropylene, carbon and stainless steel wire to create new building materials with different properties.

▲ *Composite material – this magnified picture shows fibres of glass embedded in concrete*

Reinforced concrete is everywhere – motorway bridges in Belfast, sea defences in Barcelona, houses in Berlin. Kate Hollinshead and Max Halliwell and the Building Research Establishment are providing the data that will help these structures to last longer.

▶ *Concrete-based composite boards – high-tech modern materials used to give houses an 'olde worlde' look*

1 Read 'Tube technology'. Which materials, used in making a TV tube, must
   a be strong   **b** be good electrical conductors
   c be dense   **d** have a high melting point?

2 Each year in Britain people throw away about ten million TV sets.
   Do you think there are any opportunities for setting up businesses to recycle materials from TVs and other electrical appliances? How would such businesses collect old appliances? How would they dismantle them? Which parts would be easiest to sell? Who would buy them?

3 ⚠ Take an old household electrical appliance and remove its flex. Open up the appliance by loosening screws and bolts.
   Do not break into sealed units – that could be dangerous.
   a How many different materials are used in its manufacture?
   b Estimate the masses and the financial values of the different materials. Use a computer to draw pie charts to present this information.
   c Explain how the properties of each material are matched to its use.

4 Read 'Reincarnation'.
   a Would you be more likely to buy a particular type of car if more of its components could be recycled?
   b Use a desktop publishing system to produce an advert to for a recyclable car.

5 Read 'Concrete results'.
   a When and why is reinforced concrete better than (i) solid concrete   (ii) solid steel?
   b What are the raw materials for making reinforced concrete? Draw a large diagram or poster to show the various materials. Show where they come from and how they are treated before they are brought together in concrete.
   c Look up the properties of concrete and mild steel in the Data section of this book.
   (i) Explain, in terms of atoms, why the densities of mild steel and concrete are so different.
   (ii) Estimate the volumes of 1 tonne of concrete and 1 tonne of steel. (Use density $= \dfrac{\text{mass}}{\text{volume}}$)
   (iii) How would you compare the hardness of concrete and steel?

6 ⚠ **a** Make some small sheets of concrete, with and without metal chicken wire or garden mesh to 'reinforce' them. Test the tensile strength of your sheets. Does the mesh make much difference?
   b Carry out 'accelerated tests' like those done by Kate Hollinshead. Remember that even though these tests are 'accelerated' you might have to carry out these tests over several weeks to see significant results.

7 ⚠ Repeat question 6, using sheets of concrete with and without fibre such as chopped sisal or nylon added to reinforce them.

8 Max Halliwell uses X-rays to examine crystal structure. Find out more about how X-rays create patterns that depend on the arrangements of atoms in crystals.

9 Construct a database of information about the properties of materials. Start by using the data in the table on page 172. Use your database to provide a list of materials in order, from the best electrical conductor to the worst.

10 ⚠ Look at the properties shown on pages 50 and 51. Make measurements to compare one property in two different materials, for example, tensile strength of the plastic of a crisp bag and the nylon of nylon tights.
   a Comment on the reliability of your comparisons.
   b What can you say about the structure of the materials from the properties you have observed?
   c Use the 'Reference section' of this book to compare your materials with other materials. Use a computer to create a display of this information.

11 These are the results of a test on a steel bar.

Strectching force /kN	0	5	10	15	20
Extension /μm	0	12	24	36	48

   a Plot a graph of the results, with stretching force on the x-axis.
   b Measure the gradient of the graph.
   c The gradient tells you how much the bar stretches for every kN of force. It has units $\mu m\,kN^{-1}$. An identical steel bar in a bridge is subject to a stretching force of 25 kN. According to your graph, how much is the bar stretched, compared to when it has no load?

Analysis of materials

Preparing a sample

Hazards and safety

Identifying substances and testing purity and concentration

Targets

After working through this element you should:

■ have prepared reports on the analysis of at least three different substances including one mixture, and one titration
■ be able to take a single small sample from a larger quantity of material. The sample should be representative of all of the material
■ be able to take a series of random samples of material when a single sample is unlikely to be representative
■ know the difference between elements, mixtures and compounds
■ know the difference between atoms, ions and molecules
■ be able to follow instructions and do tests to identify the following gases: carbon dioxide, hydrogen, oxygen
■ be able to follow instructions and do tests to identify the following ions:
　　chloride (Cl^-), sulphate (SO_4^{2-}), carbonate (CO_3^{2-}), sodium (Na^+), potassium, (K^+), calcium (Ca^{2+}), copper (Cu^{2+}), iron (Fe^{3+})
■ be able to follow instructions and do an acid–base titration to find the concentration of an acid or an alkali.

Key words

Some of the key technical words for this element are listed in the targets. These are some more:
molecule, positive ion, negative ion, electron, nucleus, ionic, covalent, salt, pH, indicator, end point, neutralization, solution, solvent, solute, precipitation, saturation, concentration, mole, relative atomic mass, relative formula mass.

Case study: **Fresh water, clean Aire**

▶ *The river Aire, high in the Pennine hills of Yorkshire*

▼ *People use rivers to carry away sewage and industrial waste. The river Aire passes close to Leeds, Bradford and other big towns and becomes less attractive*

Are our rivers getting cleaner or dirtier? It's the job of scientists from the National Rivers Authority to constantly monitor their condition. Here, Jeff Keenlyside describes his work on the River Aire.

'At the National Rivers Authority we run a monitoring system to check on pollution levels, taking samples from rivers at fixed intervals.

We use standardized methods of collecting and storing water samples to make sure that our comparisons are valid. It would be no good taking samples from the middle of the river one week, and the shallows the next.

If we were just starting to survey a river that nobody has checked before then we would take random samples from different places to build up a general picture. But we always use the same sites for our routine sampling programme. Each sample represents all of the water at the site.

▲ *Jenny Suter, assistant pollution control officer, working by the River Aire*

Rivers are not the safest places to work. There is always the danger of falling in, so we tell people never to go sampling alone. Bacterial contamination from sewage effluents discharged into rivers can cause infections. There may also be dangerous levels of chemical contaminants.'

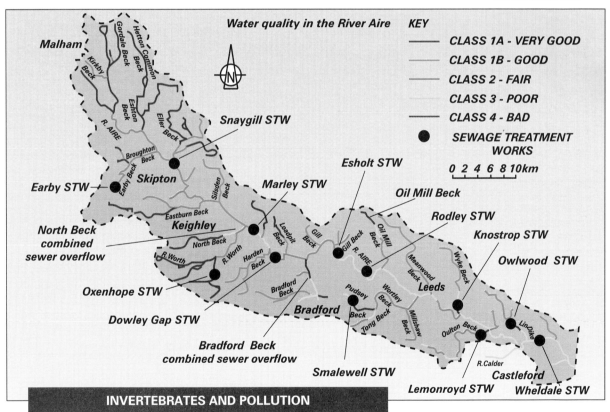

◄ *The atomic emission spectrometer measures concentrations of some important ions by detecting the light that they emit*

'Back in the lab, we carry out tests to look at the chemical composition of the water. We are looking for substances such as chlorides that make the water taste salty, or carbonates that contribute to water hardness. We also measure the pH of the water.'

'By the time the River Aire reaches Castleford it contains the outflow of many industrial users and sewage treatment works.

At the NRA we classify stretches of river. As well as using chemical tests we investigate the different invertebrates living in the river, this gives us a biological indication of the water quality. The more species there are the better the water quality.'

▲ *Treated sewage contains many materials that can affect the life of the river*

Water quality in the River Aire

KEY

———	CLASS 1A - VERY GOOD
———	CLASS 1B - GOOD
———	CLASS 2 - FAIR
———	CLASS 3 - POOR
———	CLASS 4 - BAD
●	SEWAGE TREATMENT WORKS

0 2 4 6 8 10km

INVERTEBRATES AND POLLUTION

Worms	very tolerant, found in water of poor quality
Leeches	tolerant
Freshwater shrimp	some sensitivity
Dragonfly larvae	sensitive
Most caddisfly larvae	very sensitive, only found in water of very good quality

Compounds and ions

Atoms and electricity

Atoms are units of all matter. An atom contains even smaller particles – electrons in orbit around a central nucleus. A force holds electrons close to the nucleus of an atom. We call it electric force.

We say that electrons all have 'negative' electric charge and the nucleus has 'positive' electric charge. Neutral atoms have just the right number of electrons to balance the positive charge of the nucleus. But atoms can lose or gain electrons. Either way, they then lose their electrical balance. They become charged, and we call them ions.

Elements and compounds

Elements are simple substances. In any one element all the atoms are basically the same.

Atoms of different elements have different sizes. The smallest atoms have just a single electron. The biggest have about 100. So in the whole of the universe there are only about 100 different elements.

Compounds are not so simple. There are millions of different compounds – nobody knows how many. The atoms in a compound are not all the same, and they are bonded together by electric forces of attraction.

Ionic and covalent compounds

Positive ions attract negative ions. They pull each other together into tight and orderly arrays – ionic crystals.

Atoms can also attract each other in more complicated ways. Sometimes they overlap their layers of orbiting electrons in a sharing arrangement. Then it's as if they want each other's electrons, and they will stay together to keep them. Substances that are bonded together like this are called covalent substances.

Some examples of ions

NAME OF ION	FORMULA OF ION	
Negative ions		
Chloride	Cl^-	Negative ions are non-metals
Oxide	O^{2-}	
Hydroxide	OH^-	
Sulphate	SO_4^{2-}	
Carbonate	CO_3^{2-}	
Positive ions		
Sodium	Na^+	Most positive ions are metals
Potassium	K^+	
Calcium	Ca^{2+}	
Ammonium	NH_4^+	
Copper	Cu^{2+}	
Iron	Fe^{3+}	

Note: Atoms of some elements join together in groups to form ions, like sulphate and ammonium. These groups usually stay together in chemical reactions.

Salts – ionic compounds

Salts have metal ions attracted to non-metal ions by electric force. A salt crystal is a giant structure with vast numbers of ions, each positively charged ion is surrounded by negatively charged ions.

Sodium chloride, a typical salt

| 1 | 3 | 5 | 7 | 9 | 11 | 13 |

Acids all dissolve in water and they all have a pH of less than 7

Alkalis have pH more than 7

Acids – hydrogen ion providers

When acids dissolve in water they produce solutions that always have hydrogen ions, H^+, as well as negative ions. Hydrochloric acid provides hydrogen ions and chloride ions. Sulphuric acid provides hydrogen ions and sulphate ions.

$$HCl \longrightarrow H^+ + Cl^-$$
hydrochloric acid

$$H_2SO_4 \longrightarrow 2H^+ + SO_4^{2-}$$
sulphuric acid

Bases – acid neutralizers

Some compounds can react with acids to make salts. These compounds are called bases. Most bases are insoluble in water. The small number of bases that are soluble in water are called alkalis.

Sodium hydroxide and calcium hydroxide are examples of alkalis. When alkalis dissolve they provide hydroxide ions.

$$NaOH \longrightarrow Na^+ + OH^-$$

Ions in acid-base reactions

The reaction between sodium hydroxide and hydrochloric acid can be written like this:

$$NaOH + HCl \longrightarrow NaCl + H_2O$$

We can write out the same reaction in a slightly different way, so that we can see what happens to the ions involved:

$$Na^+ + OH^- + H^+ + Cl^- \longrightarrow Na^+ + Cl^- + H_2O$$

Water is not an ionic substance. The hydrogen and the oxygen in water are not ions – they stay together by covalent bonding.

Sodium chloride is an ionic substance, its sodium and chloride ions stay in the solution. In fact, nothing has really happened to them, so we can sum up an acid–base reaction as:

$$H^+ + OH^- \longrightarrow H_2O$$

The hydrogen and hydroxide ions have reacted to make neutral water. Acid–base reactions are often called neutralization reactions.

Solutions in water

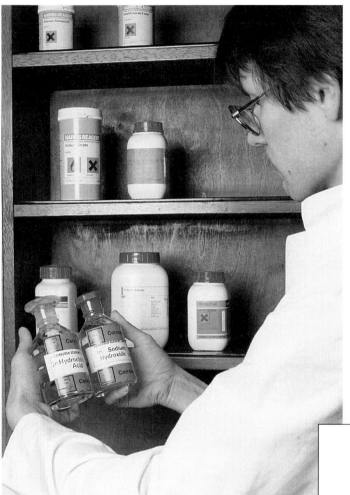

Concentration

Concentration is usually measured by the number of moles of solute in each litre of solution – the unit of measurement is moles per litre, or mol dm^{-3}. The solution of hydrochloric acid in the photo is 2 M. It contains 2 moles of hydrogen chloride for every litre of solution.

Ionic solution

Solid sodium chloride does not conduct electricity because its charged particles, the sodium and chloride ions, are stuck in a rigid crystal structure. When crystals of sodium chloride dissolve in water the ions become free from each other and can move around amongst the water molecules. Salty water is good at conducting electricity.

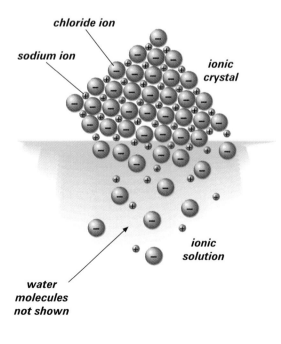

chloride ion

sodium ion

ionic crystal

ionic solution

water molecules not shown

Saturation

There is a limit to the amount of a solute that will dissolve in water. If you keep on adding solute then the solution becomes 'saturated'. More added solute just ends up at the bottom of the container. However, raising the temperature of the water will often allow more solute to dissolve before reaching saturation.

Solutions in other solvents

Some substances that are insoluble in water are soluble in other liquids. The coloured dyes in these pens, for instance, cannot be cleaned away by water. The dyes are soluble in ethanol, but not in water.

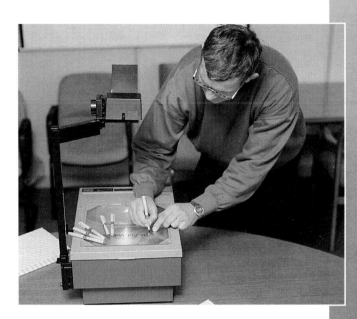

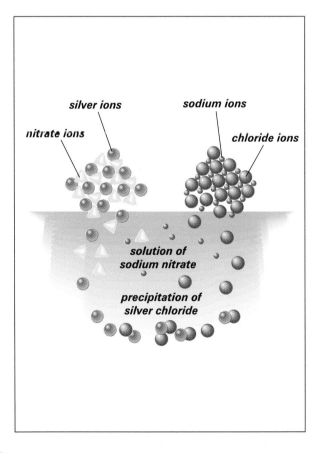

Precipitation

Sometimes if you mix solutions of two soluble salts then a reaction takes place and a new substance is made. The new substance might be insoluble in water and then it appears as a solid in the water and might slowly settle at the bottom of the container. The new solid is a precipitate.

Silver nitrate + sodium chloride $\longrightarrow$ sodium nitrate + silver chloride

Case study: The right material makes powerful medicine

▲ *Before there were antibiotics many people who were injured in war died of infections to their wounds. Penicillin saved the lives of thousands during World War II*

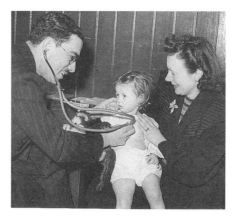

▲ *During the 1940s the healing power of the new drugs became available to everybody in the UK*

▲ *Companies like SmithKline Beecham mass-produce penicillin and other antibiotics in fermenters like this*

When antibiotics became available for the first time, around 1940, they changed people's attitudes to the power of medicines. They called them 'wonder drugs'. Bronchitis, severe acne or a wound that's gone septic – antibiotics can cure them all.

Penicillin, the very first antibiotic, is a natural substance that kills bacteria. It's made by colonies of microbes, as part of their natural life processes. Now at SmithKline Beecham they grow the microbes in huge vessels called fermenters, and then extract the penicillin.

Behind the whole manufacturing process is a team of people who make sure that the right substances, all the right materials, are in the right places. Claire Oliver, Stuart Dix, Ian Campbell and Julie Gray are four members of the team.

▲ *A course of antibiotics kills bacteria and cures infection*

◄ *Some of the people with the analytical know-how for beating disease*

Claire Oliver's pure quality

Claire Oliver monitors the identity and quality of the substances that come in from the company's suppliers.

'Most of the raw materials are things like sweeteners. We use tonnes of sugar and a whole range of flavours like orange, banana and golden syrup. We have to check that the supplier is giving us what the label says, and that we're getting the right grade. The aim is to make sure that all our raw materials are 99 to 100% pure.

Citric acid is one material that we buy in. We use it to control the pH in some of our syrups. About once every month we have to check the purity of new batches. I titrate a solution of citric acid against 0.2 M sodium hydroxide, using phenolphthalein as the indicator. The end point, when the acid and alkali exactly neutralize each other, is when the pink colour persists for about 30 seconds.'

▲ *Pouring 0.2 M sodium hydroxide into the burette*

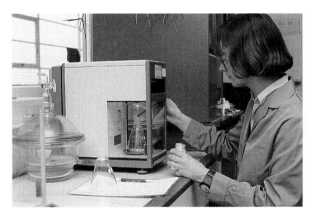

▲ *Carefully measuring the mass of citric acid – the titration will show how pure it is*

▲ *Adding a few drops of indicator*

◀ *Running the sodium hydroxide drop by drop from the burette, swirling and watching for the end point*

▼ *For some titrations a pH sensor sends information to a computer. Here, Alison Kenyon watches the screen to stay in control*

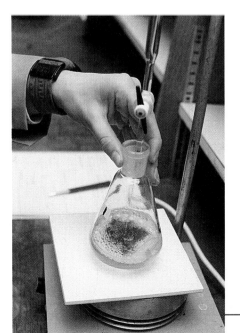

Stuart Dix – testing gas, testing growth

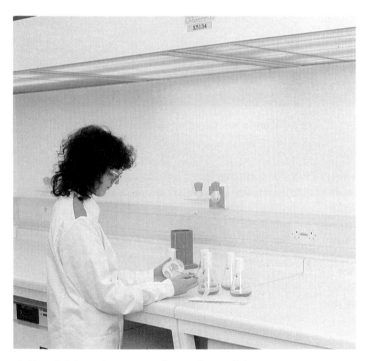

The main fermenters where microbes make penicillin are five storeys high. But Stuart Dix prepares the broth of microbes, and the food that they need, in mini-fermenters where the large scale process is simulated.

'To save money you've got to sort out problems on a smaller scale. We make sure that we've got the best conditions for growth. To control the growth we alter the stirring rate, the air supply and the temperature. Sometimes we have to add an alkali to stop the pH falling too far and killing the bugs.

The bugs produce carbon dioxide by their respiration. The faster they're growing the more carbon dioxide they produce. So we can measure their growth rate by measuring the concentration of carbon dioxide in the air from a mini-fermenter. We use a mass spectrometer for that – that ionizes the air and then shoots it through a magnetic field. Different ions follow different paths, depending on their mass, so it can show us how much there is of each type of ion.'

▲ *A mini-fermenter for creating the right conditions for rapid microbe growth*

Ian Campbell's clean air act

Ian Campbell is involved in the design and construction of specialist areas like the 'sterile room', where the air has to be as clean as it can be.

'In the sterile room people work on the microbes that we use in the fermentation process, so other kinds of microbe have to be kept out. Air inside the room comes in through filters that remove all particles above 0.3 µm in size. So the air is just the usual mixture of elements and compounds, 99.9977% free from dirt, dust and microbes.'

▲ *Very bright and very, very clean – the sterile room*

Julie Gray – keeping an ion balance

The business of growing the microbes is called fermentation. Julie Gray has the specialist knowledge of biochemistry that's needed to make the fermentation as efficient as possible.

'Inside a fermenter is a broth of microbes along with all the compounds and ions that they need for fast growth. Our 'Dionex' machine analyses the ions in samples of the broth. The machine has two columns inside. We put the sample in and one column attracts the positive ions – sodium, potassium, magnesium and calcium. The other column is positively charged and so it picks off negatively charged ions like sulphate and chloride. Then the machine washes the ions off the column. Some ions are washed off more quickly than others. We measure the concentrations of the ions by passing an electric current through the solutions. The more ions there are in a solution the more easily the current can flow.

Sulphate ions are important in penicillin, so we have to test for them every day. Basically we remove the protein from the broth and then we add barium chloride solution. Barium sulphate precipitates out and we just measure the amount of the precipitate.

The results of our tests can tell us a lot about what is going on in the fermenter. Recently we noticed that the yield of one of our products was falling off rapidly half way through the fermentation process. Our tests showed us that it was running out of chloride. We put more sodium chloride into the fermenter and the yield improved straightaway.'

Antibiotics kill bacteria without killing anything else. They're powerful medicine. The team at SmithKline Beecham make sure that the right materials are in the right place, to make sure that they make antibiotics at the right price.

▼ *Small parts at the heart of a big machine. In Julie Gray's hand are the two columns that separate the positive and negative ions*

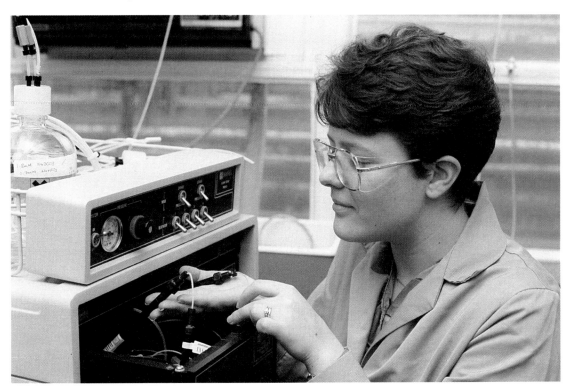

THOUGHTS AND ACTIONS

1 Read 'Clean water, clean Aire'. What precautions do NRA scientists take when they are sampling to make sure that their analysis results are reliable?

2 How many sewage treatment works empty into the River Aire above Castleford? Estimate the length of the river between Skipton and Castleford. Along what percentage of this length is the water good or very good?

3 Choose two local streams or ponds.
⚠ a Which would you expect to be more polluted? Explain why.
 b Write a list of safety precautions that are appropriate to collecting samples from these sites.
 c Work out how to collect your samples so that your comparisons will be reliable.
 d Collect samples to check your ideas on the pollution.

4 In 'The right material' the purity of citric acid (CH_3CO_2H) is checked by titrating it with sodium hydroxide (NaOH). Write a word equation for this, and also a balanced equation in symbols. See the 'Reference section' for help.

5 Write a glossary to explain all the technical terms used by Claire Oliver on page 67.

6 Draw a diagram to illustrate the principles of a Dionex machine as explained by Julie Gray on page 69.

7 a List all of the ions mentioned in 'The right material'.
 b Use the 'Reference section' to add the chemical symbol for each ion.
 c Put the information into two columns, positive ions and negative ions.
 d How does Julie Gray monitor the level of sulphate ions in the fermenter broth?

8 a How do antibiotics like penicillin work?
 b What are two major problems with the use of antibiotics nowadays and how could we overcome them?
 c In a library, research the story of the discovery of penicillin and write a short report. Would modern safety regulations have prevented the discovery?

9 Indigestion remedies, antacids, are used to
⚠ counteract excess acid in the stomach. Make a survey of the active ingredients in a number of brand name indigestion remedies. Which of the remedies seems to be best value for money? Do some tests to find out. See page 168 for help with these tests.

10 A student tested a white powder, with these results:

Tests on solid

Test	Result
Flame test	Pale mauve flame
With dilute hydrochloric acid	No gas given off

Tests on solution in water after adding nitric acid

Test	Result
With a few drops of silver nitrate	No precipitate
With a few drops of barium chloride	White precipitate

What was in the white powder?

11 Limescale ($CaCO_3$) is a problem in many places
⚠ where the water is 'hard'. Limescale forms on the elements of kettles, making them slow to boil. It also forms in sinks and toilets, where it can become ugly and provide a breeding ground for bacteria. Hardware and similar stores sell a variety of products for removing limescale, and many of these work by an acid–base reaction. Some are produced in different packaging for use in kettles and for use in toilets, etc.
 a Investigate the difference between such products. Are they the same compound at the same concentration or is there a real difference?
 b Do the differences in the products justify the differences in the way they are sold?

12 Invent an easy way of remembering the difference between molecules, atoms, ions and electrons. It could be a drawing, it could use the first letter of each word, or it could even be a poem.

Products from plants

Growing plants in the best possible conditions

Processing plant material to obtain a useful product

Economic efficiency

HARMFUL/IRRITANT

Hazards and safety

Targets

After working through this element you should:

■ have prepared a report on a product you have obtained from a plant you have grown, to show your achievement of these targets

■ be able to select a plant to grow that matches the conditions and timescale that are available to you

■ know that texture, pH, moisture, mineral nutrient levels, particle size (sand, loam or clay) and humus content are the main variables that affect the growing potential of soil

■ know that temperature range, average temperature, sunlight and water availability are the main variables that affect the growing potential of a climate

■ know about the use of sterilization, chemicals and biological control to protect plants from pests and disease

■ know that processing includes some or all of harvesting, grading, converting into the usable product, packing

■ know that in a commercial operation the cost inputs include cost of seed, labour, energy, equipment, chemicals

■ know that in a commercial operation the output can be measured by yield and by financial value

■ be able to assess the economic efficiency of your method of obtaining a product from plants, including assessment of outputs and cost inputs

Cross references

The following pages in this book will also help you to achieve these targets:

26 Giving nature a helping hand

30 Photosynthesis and nutrition

32 Reproduction and population

36 Keeping 20 million lettuces under control

177 Plant and animal nutrients

Key words

Some of the technical words for this element are listed in the targets. These are some more: cultivar, variety, fertilization, germination, propagation, photosynthesis, fertilizer, pesticide, herbicide, fungicide, insecticide, hectare, trace element, protein, nitrogen fixation, NPK, compost.

Case study: Different conditions, different crops

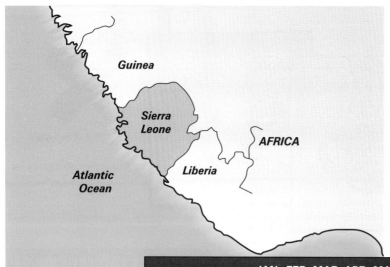

Guinea

Sierra Leone

AFRICA

Liberia

Atlantic Ocean

Area: 71000 km^2

Population: 4.2 million

Employment: Agriculture 70%, industry 14%, services 16%

Farming: Subsistence farming includes rice, maize, plantain, tomatoes, poultry, cattle and goats. Cash crops include coffee, groundnuts and ginger.

Fertilizer use: 0.4 kg/hectare/year

Climate data:

	JAN	FEB	MAR	APR	MAY	JUN	JUL	AUG	SEP	OCT	NOV	DEC
Mean rainfall/mm	10	6	27	81	229	433	869	872	652	288	138	34
Mean max temp/°C	29	30	31	30	30	29	28	28	28	29	29	29

The coffee business in Sierra Leone

Most farmers in Sierra Leone are subsistence farmers. Families grow plants and keep animals to feed themselves and they sell very little. Only about 10% of farmers grow 'cash crops' – plants grown in large quantities for selling, often for export.

One of the most important cash crops is coffee. Sierra Leone has the high temperatures, generous rainfall and good soil that suits growing coffee.

The apple business in the UK

There's a good market for apples in the UK. But only in the southern half of the country is it warm enough for apple growing to be commercially viable. Even then, 'home grown' apples have to compete with imports, mostly from other parts of the European Union, and some from as far away as New Zealand.

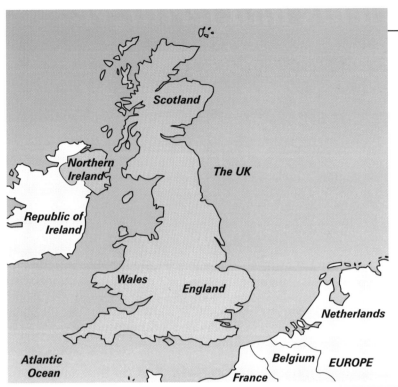

Area: 351 000 km^2

Population: 57.4 million

Employment: Agriculture 2%, industry 37%, services 61%

Farming: Self sufficient in milk and eggs, but imports much foodstuff. Barley, potatoes and wheat are main crops.

Fertilizer use: 137 kg/hectare/year

Climate data:

	JAN	FEB	MAR	APR	MAY	JUN	JUL	AUG	SEP	OCT	NOV	DEC
Mean rainfall/mm	53	42	41	44	50	54	62	61	60	67	61	57
Mean max temp/°C	6	7	10	14	17	20	22	21	19	15	10	7

Moussa Conteh, from Sierra Leone, writes about the differences between agriculture in Britain and in Sierra Leone.

We have large rivers that run down to the Atlantic Ocean. The sediment that these rivers deposit makes good fertile soil and makes it possible to grow enough food for people to eat.

There's a dry season from November or December and farmers sow their seeds at the end of April, just before the rain starts coming. July and August are the peak of the wet season, and then in September the rains start to go and fruit and seeds start to ripen.

The temperature stays almost the same all through the year, though March is about the hottest month, and that's when farmers burn the patches of land that they have prepared. That clears a lot of the pests from the soil, and nutrients from the ashes help to maintain the soil quality.

The type of farming is called 'shifting cultivation'. You clear an area of forest and farm there for one or two years. Then you leave the land fallow for between five and seven years for the soil to regain its fertility and you go on to farm somewhere else. You move around the village where you live.

Farmers mix crops together. They might grow cassava, beans and maize on the same plots as rice. Then after the main crop they grow groundnuts (peanuts) because they add nitrates to the soil. This mixed cropping has advantages over monoculture where you plant the same crop every year and rely on fertilizers to replace nutrients in the soil.

In Sierra Leone there is not the pressure on the land that you have in Europe. Traditionally, people produce food to feed themselves and their families. They don't see farming as a business like it is in Europe.

Soil, nutrients and fertilizer

Nitrogen fixers

'Nitrogen fixing bacteria' live in the soil. The gaps between the grains of soil have air as well as water. Like the air above ground, this air in the soil is mostly nitrogen. Nitrogen fixing bacteria can use the nitrogen to make nitrates.

Recycling nutrients

Small animals and microbes that live in the soil break down dead plant and animal material and turn it into humus. Compost is material that's specially collected and spread on soil to provide humus. This broken down material still contains the nutrient elements from the bodies of the dead plants and animals. Living plants can use these nutrients for their own growth.

Trace elements

Plants need very small amounts of elements like iron and magnesium. When plants and animals die, these nutrients in their bodies return to the soil. Nutrient elements can also dissolve very slowly out of solid rock. Plants can take them in through their roots. Most soil water holds traces of these elements – enough for healthy plant growth.

Manure

Manure is plant material that has been processed in the digestive system of an animal. The animal's body will have removed some of the nutrient elements from the plant for its own purposes. The calcium in a cow's milk, for example, is first extracted from grass in the cow's digestive system. Even so, manure still holds quite a lot of nutrients, and when it's spread back on the land these nutrients will support fresh plant growth.

Water and air in soil

Plants take in water through their root hairs. At the same time they take in the nutrients which are dissolved in the water. Plant roots also take in oxygen from the soil air and give out carbon dioxide. So if the soil gets waterlogged they suffer from lack of air, and if it's too dry they die from lack of water.

pH of soils

The pH of soils varies from the acidic moorland soils to alkaline chalky soils. Different types of plants grow well in these different habitats. The best soil pH for most plants and animals is about 6.5, that's slightly acid.

The texture of soils

Soil texture has to do with the size of the grains and with the amount of humus in the soil. Water drains away from the big grains of sandy soil more quickly than from the dusty grains of clay. Thick clay soils can easily get waterlogged. Loamy soil has a good grain size.

Breaking the nutrient cycle

If people grow crops in a field year after year then each year we take plant material away to eat it or for some other purpose. The nutrients in the plant material do not get the chance to return back to the soil. After just a few years crop yields will decrease drastically, unless nutrients are replaced.

NPK

There are three elements in particular that the soil can lose in just a few years if plants are not allowed to rot back into the soil. These are nitrogen (N), phosphorus (P) and potassium (K). Nearly all artificial fertilizer contains nitrogen, potassium or phosphorus, and some fertilizer contains all three.

Case study: Holly Steddon follows The Grain Trail

▲ *The start of the trail...*

▲ *...and the end of the trail*

Bread, cakes, biscuits, pasta. We all eat them. We are the consumers, and we are at the end of a long trail of events. Holly Steddon followed the trail. She explored the inputs into the business of growing grain, the variable conditions that influence wheat growth, and what happens at harvest time. She found out about buying and selling, and the standards that the grain must reach if it's to make good flour. At a mill and then at a bakery she saw two stages of processing, and in the early morning she watched trays of bread being carried away to shops and supermarkets.

◀ *Jonathan Tipples with a rich crop of wheat*

Part 1: Seed and soil

'Planting time is best. It's a new start,' Jonathan Tipples told me. He owns and manages Chainhurst Farm in Kent. 'There are a lot of decisions to be made. First of all, there's the choice between growing wheat for milling flour or wheat for animal feed. Milling wheat gets the premium prices but tends to produce low yields.'

'Then there's the variety of seed. In Scotland farmers will choose a hardy variety to combat their long winters. In the south west of England they want a variety that is resistant to fungal diseases that spread more easily in warm and moist conditions.'

Seed	22.90
Fertilizer	38.50
Herbicide (weedkiller)	25.70
Insecticide (to kill aphids)	3.40
Fungicide	16.70
Labour costs 7.3 hours at £4.80 per hour	35.00
Ploughing and power harrowing	50.00
Planting and rolling	20.00
Fertilizer application	12.00
Spraying pesticides	20.00
Combine harvesting	70.00
Carting to store	10.00
Fixed costs (rates, rent, insurance, electricity, office expenses, etc)	250.00
Total cost per hectare	574.20

Yield = 10 tonnes per hectare in a good harvest*
Price = £100 per tonne
Income = £1000 per hectare
Profit = £425.80 per hectare

*If the harvest is wet then the yield can go right down to 6 tonnes per hectare.

Jonathan is lucky, because the soil on his farm is quite loamy, a good mixture of small clay particles and large sandy grains that gives an excellent texture for the growing plants. 'Soil is our raw material,' he explained. 'The soil on this farm is in much better condition than it was 20 years ago. The phosphorus and potassium levels are balanced. The pH is corrected. That's important because if the pH of the soil wanders away from between 6.0 and 7.0 then the roots of the plants can't take up essential trace elements.'

In the farm office I saw a computer on the desk and a range of technical charts on the walls. 'Ours is a special business,' Jonathan said. 'We care for the land. We grow food, peoples' most basic need. But we also have to make a profit.'

▶ **Inputs and outputs These are the costs of growing wheat, in pounds, for every hectare of Jonathan Tipples' land.**

Part 2: The town and country link

'We're in the middle between the farmers and the people who process grain,' said Paul Smith when I met him in his office. He explained his job as 'Grain and Commodity Dealer' to me. 'We discuss with farmers what they want to grow and how much of it. They could go for the quality market where the grain will be used to make flour or they could go for the animal feedstock market. We advise the farmers about the state of the market and find out whether they want to sell their crop at harvest time for a quick return or store it until the price is right.'

'Apart from the small samples that we test in our lab, we never see the crop. Some grain is exported, mainly to European countries. At the moment we are negotiating to send 20 000 tonnes to China. In this job you have to have your heart in the country, and your head in the City to keep an eye on the market.'

▼ **Keeping up with changing market prices**

▲ *Taking samples from another lorry load of grain*

Part 3: Breaking, grinding, separating

Joan Davis, the Supervisor in the analytical labs at Bugbrooke Mills, explained the reason for the bustle. 'Thirty to forty lorries of wheat pull up outside our lab every day. We test grain samples from each lorry coming to the mill in a whole range of different ways and all within fifteen minutes.'

'We measure protein content and quality, moisture and hardness of the grain. Then we need to know how much chaff, shriveled grain, or grain of the wrong kind there is. We call this material the screenings. We sieve the grain and if the screenings amounts to more than 3% of the load then it could all be rejected. And if we see beetles, weevils or mites then we don't let the load go any further.'

Once the tests are done the lorries move on and tip their loads in the right silos for blending and then for the milling itself. Milling involves a sequence of breaking, grinding and separating. The grain is torn but not squashed in rollers with different types of teeth or fluting. Then it's sifted and the finer grains go into rollers which flatten the particles and turn them into flour. The larger grains go back into the system to be torn up and sifted again. Grain keeps going through this process until 78% of it ends up as flour. The rest is bran and germ that's used for wholemeal flour or to make breakfast cereals or animal feed. Nothing is wasted.

Part 4: First light at Pegrum's bakery

It was barely 6.00 in the morning and the smell of freshly baked bread enveloped the whole area. Outside, the first light of the day was shining on the silo where the white flour is kept, and on the inside the trays of bread and pastry were lined up ready for the shops.

Nigel Pegrum let me into some of the secrets of making bread. 'It's all in the flour,' he said. 'The dough would just fall apart if the flour wasn't strong with a high protein content – about 12%. We use imported Canadian flour to give us this protein level. On the prairies there is the good seed and soil combined with the best possible climate of hard winters and good summers for growing grain.'

We watched a dough maker expertly adding just the right amount of water to a mixture of flour, margarine, yeast, yeast food and salt. Nigel told me about the small brown pellets of compressed yeast. 'Yeast is live and it has to be treated gently to give the best results. We use treacle, caramel or dextrose as food for the yeast, depending on the type of bread we're baking.'

We moved out to look at the heart of the bakery, the oven. Inside the oven the little bubbles of carbon dioxide made by the yeast would expand and the dough would stiffen into fine crusty bread.

▼ *A lesson in the doughs and don'ts of baking good bread*

Case study: Some Secretts of success

▲ *The Secrett flower shop*

Helen Davies, Chris Briant and Simon Lambert are all GNVQ students at Woking College in Surrey. To find out more about growing and selling products from plants they got in touch with Secretts, who've been growing plants since 1908. The company has survived all that time by being ready to change. In fact they've often led the way – one of their latest moves is to be the first company in mainland Britain to grow and market such a wide range of flowers by post.

The company moved to Surrey in 1938. The site they chose had rather poor sandy soil and needed to have a lot of added humus. But it was reasonably close to London and to the coast for exporting their produce. Then in the 1970s, growers used more mechanization and more fertilizers and they were getting more produce per hectare. The result was that prices dropped and many people went out of business. But Secretts opened a garden centre, then a farm shop, a delicatessen and began pick-your-own marketing. Business thrived.

In the shop they were selling flowers from Holland. But the family had the expertise for growing as well as for retail selling. So, over three years, they carried out a feasibility study. They learnt more about Dutch growing methods, such as greenhouse automation and storing cut plants in water. Now they have two and a half acres of greenhouse and grow flowers all the year round.

Helen Davies looked at the inputs and the costings involved.

'Chrysanthemums arrive at Secretts' nursery as little cuttings costing 5p each. For successful cultivation they need water, light, P/D control (P/D means pest and disease), good soil with a lot of nutrients, a steady temperature of about 17 °C and a lot of carbon dioxide.

They grow 64 plants in every square metre of soil, at a rate of four crops per year. Eighty to ninety percent of the plants reach flowering. Labour and sprays – that's P/D control and fertilizer – are the main costs. Each square metre needs an average of 0.55 hours' work in each year, at an agricultural wage of £3.55 per hour. Then fertilizer costs 70p per year per square metre, and pesticide is 60p per year per square metre. The wholesale price is £1.50 per bunch, that's five plants.'

▲ *Helen Davies checks data from the computer*

Simon Lambert explains about control of light and carbon dioxide level.

'If the glass of the greenhouses is kept clean then 60 to 75% of the light that's useful for photosynthesis will get through to the plants. At Secretts they control the light by screening it out or by using artificial light. That way, with the help of their heating system, they can grow four crops each year, one in the winter and three in the summer.

The air in the greenhouse has 1000 parts per million of carbon dioxide. That's three times the normal concentration of carbon dioxide in the air outside. The high amount of carbon dioxide speeds up photosynthesis.'

▼ *Simon Lambert with environmental monitoring and control equipment*

Chris Briant looked at harvesting, storing and packaging.

◀ *Chris Briant learns how the packaging goes together*

▶ *The packaging has to be good enough to make sure that flowers arrive in perfect condition*

'The plants are harvested whenever they are ready. In Holland they do that by machine but Secretts grow different varieties, of different heights. The storage area is cold and dark and plants stay there for up to 48 hours with their stems in water.

Secretts sell about half of the flowers in their own shop, and most of the rest to local shops and florists. Now they're building up their postal flower sales, which needs special packaging for the flowers. Moist tissue is wrapped around the bottom of the stems, and a moisture-proof wrap goes on top of that. There's a protective film of cellophane and then the flowers are fastened to a cardboard inner sleeve. That fits into a decorated box with a cellophane window. There's a conditioner pack with a pH regulator, and a bactericide. Finally, the decorated box goes into an outer sleeve.'

THOUGHTS AND ACTIONS

1 a Identify some different types of pest control in the three case studies in this chapter.

   b Why do different plant growers use different techniques? What are their advantages and disadvantages?

   c In Indonesia in the 1980s farmers used a massive programme of spraying to try to kill off the brown planthopper insects that damaged their rice crops. It didn't work, and worse still it destroyed many of the spiders and other insects which naturally eat the brown planthoppers. Then between 1986 and 1988 an integrated pest management programme was introduced. This used some chemical pest control alongside biological control. The results of the scheme are shown here.

   Amounts of insecticide applied to rice:
   1986 – insecticide applied an average of 4.3 times per crop
   1988 – insecticide applied an average of 0.4 times per crop.
   Insecticide costs in Indonesian rupiah:
   1986 – 35 000 rupiah per hectare
   1988 – 6000 rupiah per hectare
   Rice yield:
   1986 – 5.9 tonnes per hectare
   1988 – 7.9 tonnes per hectare

   (i) Use a computer to generate graphic displays of this information.
   (ii) Produce a paper which explains the benefits of an integrated pest management scheme to a government which is spending very large sums of money helping farmers to buy insecticides.

2 Farming practices in Sierra Leone and the United Kingdom are different in many ways.
   a Draw up a table to show these differences.
   b Present the climate data for Sierra Leone and the UK in graphic form.
   c Which of the differences in farming practices are due to differences in climate?
   d What other factors are there that influence farming practices?
   e How could farming practices in the UK be improved? How could farming practices in Sierra Leone be improved? What would be the difficulties in making these improvements?

3 Use the information in the 'Grain trail' to make a flow diagram illustrating the steps in the production of bread, starting from seed. Show inputs at each of the stages, e.g. seed, labour, energy, equipment, chemicals.

4 Some people say that farmers should grow food 'organically' – without using pesticides or fertilizers.
   Use the information in 'The Grain Trail' to write about the pressures on farmers to use these substances.

5 Enter the data of yield and profitability of Jonathan Tipples' farm onto a spreadsheet and use the spreadsheet to work out the effects of a wet year.

6 Jonathan Tipples pays a soil testing laboratory to ⚠ analyse the soil from his fields so that he knows how to treat the soil.
   a Collect soil from three different places and compare the samples in as many ways as you can.
   b What should you look for in your soil samples that might indicate high or low levels of nitrogen?
   c Why is nitrogen so important?

7 a In Secrett's greenhouses they plant 64 plants per square metre. What is the cost of their cuttings per square metre per crop?
   b What are the labour costs per square metre per crop?
   c What are the costs of fertilizer and pesticide per square metre per crop?
   d Other costs come to £2.50 per square metre per crop. What is the profit per square metre per crop?
   e What is the annual profit per square metre?

8 In a group, design a set of experiments on the ⚠ effects of various possible useful substances that could be added to the water used for growing cress from seed. Each member of the group should do one experiment from the set and you should prepare a combined report. The report should include spreadsheet, tables of data and computer generated graphics.

Products from reactions

Preparing useful materials

Separating out the required products

Working out yields and costs

CORROSIVE

Hazards and safety

Targets

After working through this element you should:

- have prepared products from at least three reactions to show your achievement of these targets
- know how to prepare a salt using an acid–base reaction
- know how to prepare an insoluble salt using a precipitation reaction
- know how to prepare an ester
- know how to prepare a pure metal using a redox reaction
- know how to use filtration, crystallization and distillation to isolate and purify products that you have prepared
- be able to calculate the theoretical and percentage yield of products of reactions
- be able to estimate the cost of raw materials, energy, labour and equipment for the materials that you have prepared
- know that salts are made in reactions between bases and acids
- know that esters are made in reactions between alcohols and organic acids
- know that these esterification reactions are reversible and require a catalyst to ensure a good yield of product
- know that oxidation takes place when oxygen is added to a substance and that reduction takes place when oxygen is removed from a substance
- know that oxidation and reduction occur together and the whole reactions are called redox reactions.

Key words

Some of the key technical words for this element are listed in targets. These are some more:
reactant, product, actual yield, pH, neutralization, ion, relative atomic mass, relative formula mass, mole, alkane.

Case study: White powders for everything

White powder 1

People like their make-up and personal care products to be smooth and soft. Some of Allied Colloids' polymers are added to products like moisturizers and liquid soap to give them their creamy consistency.

'All our products make other things work better – they're performance enhancers,' said Marcus Kendall. He works at Allied Colloids, a large chemicals company based in Bradford. 'A lot of local people have little idea about what we make because our products all look like very ordinary white powders and colourless liquids. Everything we produce goes to other industries, from sugar refining to paper making.'

White powder 2

Allied Colloids make 'flocculents'. These are powders with long chain molecules that are big enough to wrap themselves around tiny grains suspended in sewage. They make the grains in the sewage stick together, so that they settle out of the water more quickly.

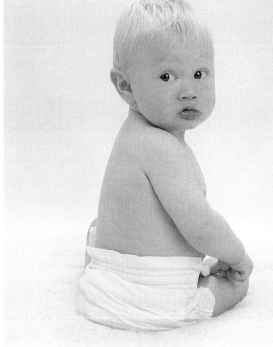

White powder 3

Salsorb is a powder that goes into babies' nappies. It's biodegradable and completely harmless, and some grades can absorb up to 500 times their own mass of water.

White powder 4

Fine powders can help solids and liquids to mix evenly. China manufacturers use products from Bradford to disperse the clay evenly in water. The result is better quality china with no faults or bubbles. And it's cheaper.

White powder 5

Dispersants make sure that the pigment in paint remains evenly spread.

'One of our main starting materials is called acrylonitrile,' says Colin Kenning, a Laboratory Manager at Allied Colloids. 'We buy it in from other companies and react it with water, speeding up the reaction by using a copper catalyst and a high temperature.'

$$\text{acrylonitrile} + \text{water} \xrightarrow[\substack{\text{high} \\ \text{temperature}}]{\substack{\text{copper catalyst} \\ \text{and}}} \text{acrylamide}$$

Some acrylamide goes to make flocculents and we react some with more water to make acrylic acid for Salsorb and many other products.

$$\text{acrylamide} + \text{water} \longrightarrow \text{acrylic acid}$$

'Part of our job is to make sure that we get a high yield. That means as much of the acrylonitrile as possible has to be converted into useful end product. It makes a big difference to the profitability of the company – there are thousands of pounds at stake every week.

In the week ending 12 December, for example, we used 188 tonnes of acrylonitrile to manufacture 228 tonnes of acrylic acid. To know how good that is we have to work out what the theory says we should get. That means using the chemical formulas of the various substances.

Acrylonitrile is CH_2CHCN
Acrylic acid is CH_2CHCO_2H

Now we can use these to count up the relative formula masses. Hydrogen atoms count as 1 unit, carbon counts as 12 units, nitrogen counts as 14 units and oxygen counts as 16 units (see Reference section pages 166 and 176). So:

Acrylonitrile has 3 units for hydrogen, 36 units for carbon and 14 units for nitrogen. That's a total relative formula mass of 53 units.

Acrylic acid has 4 units for hydrogen, 36 units for carbon and 32 units for oxygen, which comes to a relative formula mass of 72 units.

A molecule of acrylonitrile makes a molecule of acrylic acid. But in real chemistry we can't count every single molecule. We have to deal with huge numbers of molecules, so we talk about moles. A mole is just an amount of substance with a certain number of basic particles like atoms on molecules.

The special thing about a mole is that the mass of a mole of any substance, in grams, is the same number as the relative formula mass. A mole of acrylonitrile has a mass of 53 g, and a mole of acrylic acid has a mass of 72 g. Then the logic goes like this:

1 molecule of acrylonitrile makes 1 molecule of acrylic acid

so 1 mole of acrylonitrile makes 1 mole of acrylic acid

so 53 g of acrylonitrile makes 72 g of acrylic acid.

We can scale that up into tonnes:

53 tonnes of acrylonitrile makes 72 tonnes of acrylic acid.

We can scale that up again, to match the amount of acrylonitrile we actually used in that week:

188 tonnes of acrylonitrile makes 255 tonnes of acrylic acid.

Notice that the calculations don't agree with the yield of acrylic acid we actually got. We only got 228 tonnes. One cause of that is that we don't succeed in separating all of the acrylic acid from the mixture in the reactors.

actual yield = 228 tonnes

theoretical yield = 255 tonnes

$$\text{percentage} = \frac{228}{255} \times 100\% = 89\%'$$

Making salts

Salts are ionic compounds. They contain positive ions and negative ions, and are crystalline solids.

The method for making a salt will depend on whether the various substances involved, reactants and products, are soluble in water.

Making soluble salts

Method 1 – with an acid and a base that's insoluble in water

Many bases are insoluble in water so you have to add the solid material to the acid.
Example:
Magnesium oxide is an insoluble base that reacts with sulphuric acid to make magnesium sulphate. Magnesium sulphate is a salt used to help fabrics to absorb dyes.

sulphuric acid + magnesium oxide ⟶
magnesium sulphate + water

$$H_2SO_4 + MgO \longrightarrow MgSO_4 + H_2O$$

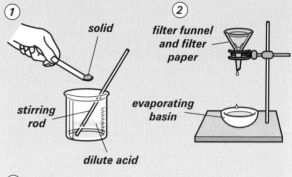

① solid
stirring rod
dilute acid

② filter funnel and filter paper
evaporating basin

③ ④

Step 1 Add the solid bit by bit until no more will react – you'll be able to see solid left in the solution.

Step 2 Filter the solution to remove any unreacted solid.

Step 3 Heat the solution gently to speed up the evaporation of water. Wear safety glasses. Crystals of the salt will form around the edges of the solution.

Step 4 Put the solution aside to allow the crystals to grow slowly as the rest of the water evaporates.

Method 2 – with an acid and a base that's soluble in water

A base that's soluble in water is called an alkali.
Example:
Sodium hydroxide is an alkali that reacts with sulphuric acid to make sodium sulphate. It's a salt that's used in glass making.

sulphuric acid + sodium hydroxide ⟶
sodium sulphate + water

$$H_2SO_4 + 2NaOH \longrightarrow Na_2SO_4 + 2H_2O$$

If a compound being added to the acid is soluble in water then you can't tell when the reaction is complete. You could easily add more of the substance than is necessary for making sure that all the acid has reacted. The excess substance will contaminate the salt you are making.

An indicator will stop this happening, by showing when you've added just enough alkali to neutralize the acid – just enough alkali to react with the acid to produce a salt solution that is neither acidic nor alkaline.

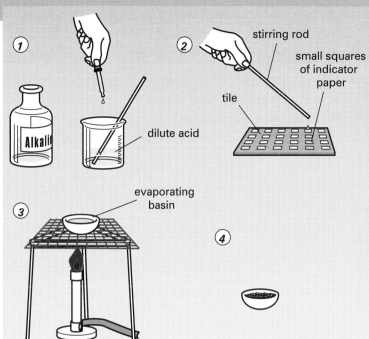

Step 1 Add alkali slowly and keep stirring the liquid.

Step 2 Test pH at regular intervals by transferring a drop of the solution on to indicator paper. Keep doing this until the solution is neutral.

Step 3 Heat the solution gently to speed up the evaporation of the water. Wear safety glasses. Crystals of salt form around the edges of the solution.

Safety note It is important that you only do this with neutral solution. An acidic or alkaline solution can give off harmful fumes.

Step 4 Set the solution aside and allow the crystals to grow slowly.

Making salts that are insoluble in water

Example:
Barium sulphate doesn't let X-rays pass through it. After a patient has swallowed a 'barium meal' it's possible to follow the salt through their intestines. You can make barium sulphate by a reaction between two soluble salts. It's called a 'precipitation' reaction.

Barium chloride is soluble in water. Its crystals break up into free ions when they dissolve. In this case you get barium, Ba^+, and chloride , Cl^-, ions. In the same way, magnesium sulphate separates into magnesium ions, Mg^{2+}, and sulphate ions, SO_4^{2-}.

So if you add a solution of barium chloride and a solution of magnesium sulphate you get a soup of four different ions. When barium and sulphate ions come together they start to form insoluble crystals of barium sulphate. The magnesium and chloride ions stay in the solution.

A summary of the reaction is:

barium chloride + magnesium sulphate ⟶ barium sulphate + magnesium chloride

$$BaCl_2 + MgSO_4 \longrightarrow BaSO_4 + MgCl_2$$

or, the same thing showing the separate ions:

$$Ba^{2+} + 2Cl^- + Mg^{2+} + SO_4^{2-} \longrightarrow$$
$$BaSO_4(solid) + Mg^{2+} + 2Cl^-$$

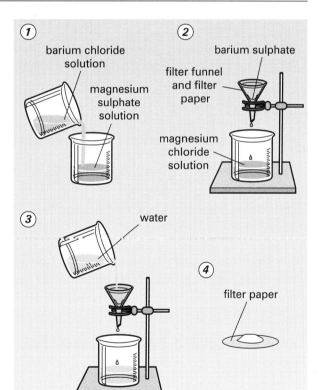

Step 1 Mix the solutions of two soluble salts.

Step 2 Filter off the precipitate of the insoluble salt.

Step 3 Wash the precipitate with water.

Step 4 Leave the precipitate to dry at room temperature or in an oven.

Redox reactions

Redox is short for reduction and oxidation. A redox reaction goes on in a blast furnace where iron is separated from iron ore.

Iron ore is mostly iron oxide which is a hard red substance that's not much good for making cars or bridges or knives and forks. The iron and the oxygen must be separated – the iron oxide must be 'reduced'. Carbon monoxide will do the job, acting as a 'reducing agent'.

$$Fe_2O_3 + 3CO \longrightarrow 2Fe + 3CO_2$$

iron oxide + carbon monoxide ⟶

iron + carbon dioxide

The iron has lost its oxygen, but the carbon monoxide has gained it and turned into carbon dioxide. The carbon monoxide has been oxidized. Reduction and oxidation take place together. If something is losing oxygen then some other substance must be gaining it.

The thermit reaction

The violent 'thermit' reaction is a redox reaction between iron oxide and aluminium. The reaction is the basis of one method of welding.

Reduction of iron oxide liberates iron.

$$Fe_2O_3 + 2Al \longrightarrow 2Fe + Al_2O_3$$

Aluminium is oxidised.

iron oxide + aluminium ⟶ **iron + aluminium oxide**

The aluminium reduces the iron oxide to liberate the iron. Or, if you prefer, the iron oxide oxidizes the aluminium. Either way it's highly exothermic – it makes energy available. In fact the materials become so hot that the iron is molten, and as it cools it welds together pieces of steel.

Ions and electrons in the thermit reaction

We can write out the thermit reaction to show the ions involved:

$$2Fe^{3+} + 3O^{2-} + 2Al \longrightarrow 2Fe + 2Al^{3+} + 3O^{2-}$$

The oxygen ions haven't changed at all.

Each atom of iron has gained three electrons and changed from a positive ion into a neutral atom. The iron atoms are no longer attracted to the oxygen. The iron has been set free.

The aluminium atoms have each lost three electrons to become positive ions. Now they are attracted to the oxygen ions.

The special chemistry of carbon

Carbon forms covalent compounds. Its atoms share their outer electrons with atoms of hydrogen, oxygen and other elements. Carbon atoms will also share electrons with other carbon atoms to make long chains. The special chemistry of carbon is at the heart of the special chemistry of all living things.

Families of carbon compounds

There are millions of compounds with the element carbon in them. Fortunately, we can group carbon compounds into families like the alkanes, the alcohols and the organic acids.

Alkanes	Alcohols	Organic Acids

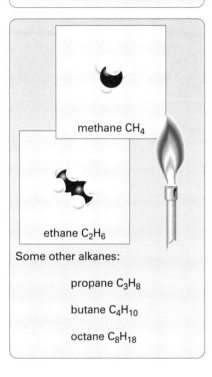

methane CH_4

ethane C_2H_6

Some other alkanes:

propane C_3H_8

butane C_4H_{10}

octane C_8H_{18}

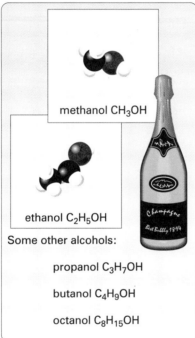

methanol CH_3OH

ethanol C_2H_5OH

Some other alcohols:

propanol C_3H_7OH

butanol C_4H_9OH

octanol $C_8H_{15}OH$

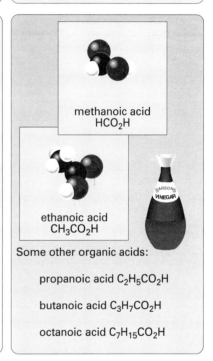

methanoic acid HCO_2H

ethanoic acid CH_3CO_2H

Some other organic acids:

propanoic acid $C_2H_5CO_2H$

butanoic acid $C_3H_7CO_2H$

octanoic acid $C_7H_{15}CO_2H$

Esterification – a carbon chemistry reaction

Esters are another family of carbon compounds. One of the smallest members of the family is ethyl ethanoate. It has a fruity smell and we use it as a solvent in nail polish. It can be made by the reaction between ethanol and ethanoic acid.

ethanol + ethanoic acid $\rightleftharpoons$ ethyl ethanoate + water

$C_2H_5OH + CH_3CO_2H \rightleftharpoons CH_3CO_2C_2H_5 + H_2O$

•We have to write the reaction with a double headed arrow because it is reversible. Ethyl ethanoate can combine with water to make ethanoic acid and ethanol.

•The reaction takes place slowly, even at high temperature. But concentrated sulphuric acid can speed the reaction up without actually changing itself. The sulphuric acid is then acting as a catalyst.

•All esterification reactions follow the same pattern. For example,

methanol + propanoic acid $\rightleftharpoons$
methyl propanoate + water

$CH_3OH + C_2H_5CO_2H \rightleftharpoons C_2H_5CO_2CH_3 + H_2O$

We can sum up the esterification pattern by,

alcohol + organic acid $\rightleftharpoons$ ester + water

Case study: Perfumes for people

▶ **Perfumes from Givaudan-Roure are important in personal care products and also in products like fly spray and toilet cleaner**

▲ **Grasse, home of the perfume industry**

Grasse is a town in Southern France, in the warm hills not far from the Mediterranean Sea. For more than 500 years it has been a centre of perfume production. The local farmers grow roses, jasmine, lavender and many other plants for their natural perfume ingredients. But most modern perfume ingredients do not come from flowers.

Most people could not afford to buy perfumes made only with chemicals extracted from plants. The extracts are very expensive because of the long production processes and low yields. Perfumes became available to more people, for everyday soaps and cosmetics, when companies like Givaudan-Roure began making synthetic aroma chemicals on a large scale.

The houses of Givaudan and Roure were founded in the nineteenth century, when the idea of synthetic chemicals was still very new. Perfumers were used to dealing only with precious natural ingredients, and they were doubtful about the new products. But now there is a whole industry devoted to the synthesis of chemicals for perfume.

▲ *The Givaudan-Roure factory – esterification in progress,*

phenyl ethanol + **ethanoic acid** ⇌ **phenyl ethyl ethanoate** + **water**
(a type of alcohol)   *(a type of*   *(a type of ester)*
               organic acid)

A lot of the chemicals used by perfumers are esters. There are many different esters, and their individual names seem to be very different to the pleasant fragrances that we experience from them. Phenyl ethyl ethanoate is one ester. It has a rich odour, with a smooth honey-like character.

At Givaudan-Roure they make phenyl ethyl ethanoate from phenyl ethanol, which is a kind of alcohol. It's used in rose perfume and for flavouring Turkish delight. A reaction with ethanoic acid converts it into the ester with a richer, stronger fragrance. Water is produced at the same time.

The reaction is reversible, and Givaudan-Roure need to prevent the ester and water turning back into alcohol and acid. So they remove the water from the reaction vessels as quickly as it forms.

The newly formed ester collects in the upper layers of the reaction mixture. It is impure, still containing leftover ethanoic acid and phenyl ethanol. They distill the impure mixture, so that the ester boils away into another vessel and leaves the impurities behind.

▲ *Distillation provides pure ester from an impure mixture*

People like perfumes. Fragrances affect our moods and our thoughts. At Givaudan-Roure they make perfumes in huge quantities. Their perfumes help to make us feel good about many products that we use, from toilet cleaners to body sprays.

1 Write a glossary to help readers to understand the 'White powders' case study. Include these words:
- biodegradable
- colloid
- dispersant
- flocculent
- hydrolysis
- moisturizer
- molecule
- polymer
- viscous
- relative formula mass
- yield.

2 The products of Allied Colloids ('White powders') all look much the same but they do many different jobs. Design an advertising poster to explain the work of Allied Colloids to the public.

3 Read about yield calculation in 'White powders' and on page 166 in the 'Reference section', and read about making esters in 'Perfumes for people'. The esterification reaction used by Givaudan-Roure is:

phenyl ethanol + ethanoic acid $\longrightarrow$
    phenyl ethyl ethanoate + water
$C_8H_9OH + CH_3CO_2H \longrightarrow CH_3CO_2C_8H_9 + H_2O$

a What is the relative formula mass of each of these four substances?

b What is the mass, in units, of 1 molecule of each of the substances?

c What is the mass in grams of 1 mole of each of the substances?

d If a reaction uses 60 g of ethanoic acid, how much phenyl ethanol does it use, and how much of the ester does it produce if the reaction is complete and no ester is lost? This is the theoretical yield.

e If Givaudan-Roure only produce 150 g of the ester for every 60 g of ethanoic acid they use, what is the percentage yield?

f Suggest why the percentage yield is not 100%.

4 **a** How is it possible for the mass of acrylic acid made by Allied Colloids to be bigger than the mass of acrylonitrile that they use?

b Which element is a contituent of acrylonitrile but not of acrylic acid? Can you suggest what might happen to this element during the manufacture of acrylic acid?

5 'Women are generally more sensitive to smells than men.' Is this true? Is 'sensitivity' something that you can measure? Decide what you think 'sensitivity' means. Devise a way of testing the statement, using different perfumes. Try out your method on a suitable group of people. Is it possible to reach valid conclusions about the statement?

6 **a** Carry out a survey of all the perfumed products in your home.

b Which of these products are necessities and which are luxuries?

c Devise and carry out a survey to find out whether or not people's choice of product is affected by the smell.

7 Use steam distillation to extract the perfume from dried lavender flowers.

a Try to estimate the yield of perfume and compare it with the mass of flowers you started with.

b How much would it cost to produce enough perfume to sell? Take account of labour costs, energy costs and the raw materials.

c What would you charge for this perfume and how would you market it?

8 Write word equations for the formation of perfume esters from these acids and alcohols:
a amyl salicylate from amyl alcohol and salicylic acid.
b vetyvenyl acetate from the alcohol vetyvenol and acetic acid.

9 Make a range of simple esters by reacting organic acids with alcohols. Describe the various odours.

10 **a** Use the information in the chapter to give a general description and two examples of these types of reactions;
(i) redox   (ii) acid-base

b Use other sources to describe one more example of each of these types of reaction. Write word equations and formula equations for each example. Also explain the reactions in terms of ions and electrons, as for the thermit reaction on page 92.

Electrical and electronic devices

Describing the purpose of devices and their main parts

Assembling and testing devices

Working safely

Targets

After working through this element you should:

- have built two devices; one or both devices should be electronic
- have described the purpose of the devices and of each of their parts
- have tested the reliability, accuracy, effectiveness, sensitivity and portability (as appropriate) of the devices
- know that purposes of electrical and electronic devices can include moving, communicating, warning, measuring and contolling
- understand that for an electrical device we can draw a single circuit diagram with symbols to represent every component
- understand that for electronic devices it is usually easier to represent the parts of the device by blocks with written descriptions of their purposes
- be able to identify the following parts in real devices and in diagrams: resistor, switch, power source, thermistor, LDR, diode, transistor, logic gate, IC, relay, voltmeter, ammeter, lamp, LED, motor, heater, buzzer
- be able to set up electrical circuits that consist of a single loop (series circuits) and to measure the voltage across the components
- know that devices need a suitable power source
- know that electronic devices have one or more input units such as sensors or switches
- know that electronic devices have processor units such as logic gates, ICs (integrated circuits) or timers
- know that electronic devices have one or more output units such as LEDs, motors, heaters or buzzers.

Cross references

The following pages in this book will also help you to achieve these targets:

Key words

Some of the technical words for this element are listed in the targets. These are some more: potential difference or voltage, volt (V), current, amp (A), milliamp (mA), resistance, ohm (Ω), positive, negative, signal, logic state, transducer, transducer driver, frequency.

Case study: **Light work**

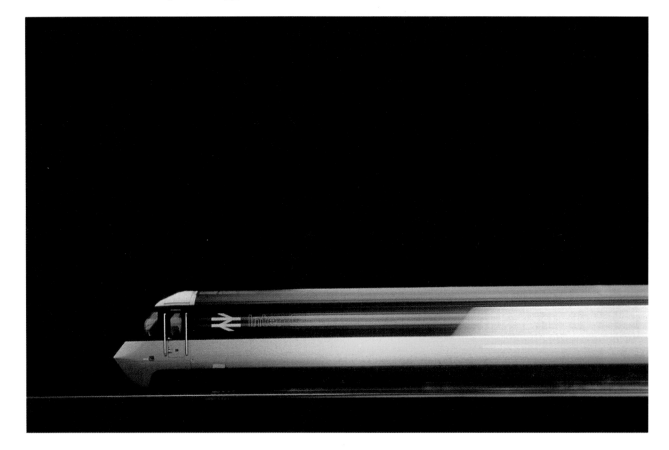

If a train has a headlight that doesn't work then it doesn't run. That's part of the safety-first policy on the UK rail network. But a train out of action can cause a lot of disruption, so to improve both safety and efficiency Hugh Barton has been developing a new kind of portable lamp that can be fitted to a train at a moment's notice.

Hugh is an optical physicist at the Rail Research Centre in Crewe, Cheshire. Before he got this job he studied Applied Physics at the University of Coventry and spent a year in Germany working on research into the future possibilities of nuclear fusion. 'Most of the optics that I use on a day-to-day basis is what I've learnt working here,' he says. 'The most challenging part is not the optics but the special requirements of the railway environment, such as safety specifications and the practical ease of use and servicing of the devices that I work on.'

The front of a train is not a friendly place, so the specification for the new lamp was very demanding. Portable, reliable, waterproof, robust, able to work at any angle, and provide a beam that can be seen by a lookout in a track crew at a distance of up to 800 metres. That was Hugh's challenge. 'We had to create a unit that could take a lot of knocks in it's everyday use,' he says. 'The optical part of the system is fairly straightforward to design once you've got a feel for the specification. It was the battery and the casing that presented the special problems.'

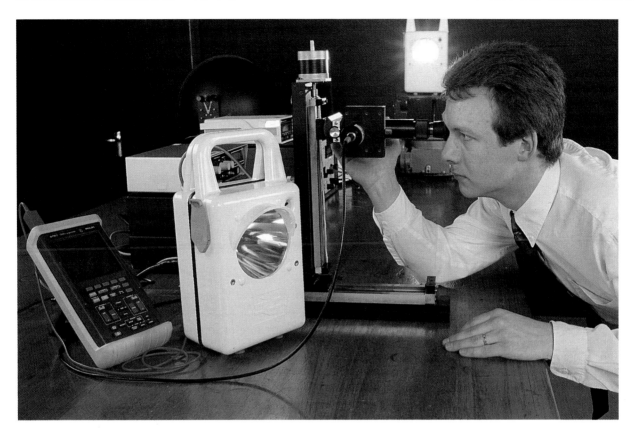

▲ *Hugh Barton working on the portable lamp*

He works at a lab bench to try out ideas and measure the properties of the components he wants to use. Then he turns to a computer which can do a lot of the boring and repetitive work, including calculations. A big benefit of computers is for modelling – predicting the outcome of using a different kind of light source, for example, without having to set the whole thing up. Since every situation is different Hugh has to write his own computer programmes for that sort of thing.

The combination of lab measurements and computer models should produce a device that has the ideal materials working in harmony. 'Every component has to have the right blend of properties, and simplicity is important. There's no point in using anything too sophisticated – it could just add to the cost whilst reducing reliability. Take the lens. It's just a flat piece of polycarbonate, but it has to combine the right amount of rigidity and resistance to impact with the ability to transmit light. A thickness of 3 mm is about ideal.'

'The battery was more difficult,' says Hugh, 'We chose a lead-acid battery because it is rechargeable, like in a car. But you can't turn a car battery upside down because the acid electrolyte is liquid and it will run out. The battery we selected is a sealed unit, with the electrolyte held closely around the lead plates.'

Railway staff need to be able to go to a storeroom and pick up a lamp knowing that it will work. So Hugh designed circuits to provide information about the condition of the lamp. If the battery has got less than about 4 hours of life left in it then an LED lights up and the unit will have to be recharged before it's used. If the lamp doesn't work at all then it's important to know what the problem is. Another LED lights up if the filament breaks, to show that nothing more than a new light bulb is needed.

'Once I'd worked out the principles of the unit I produced a working prototype and a design specification for the manufacturers to work on. Part of my job is to consult with the manufacturers to make sure that they can finish off the detail of the design, keeping costs as low as possible.'

'As for testing general robustness, the prototype had to be dropped from a height of 1 metre onto concrete. Then it went through vibration tests, mounted on a special table and shaken at a range of frequencies and amplitudes. To see that the design is waterproof the manufacturer created a vacuum inside the casing and then immersed the whole thing in water.'

Every driver in a train, watching for signs on the line ahead, needs light to see. People working on the line need 25 seconds from seeing the light of an approaching train to safely clear the line. Hugh Barton provides the light.

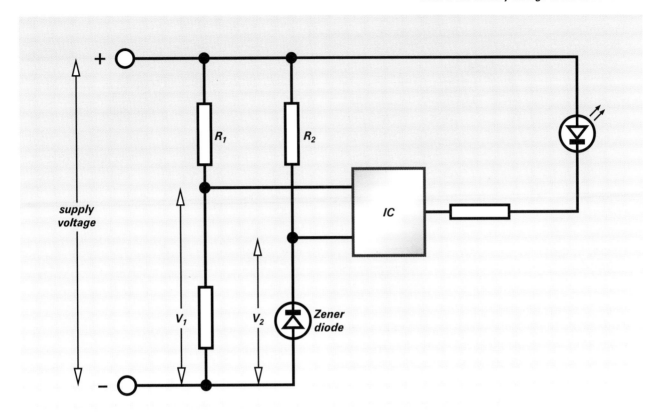

The IC compares the two voltages, V_1 and V_2. If V_1 is bigger than V_2 then the LED stays off. The special Zener diode is there to make sure that V_2 doesn't change very much. If the total battery voltage falls below about 11 V then V_1 becomes less than V_2 and the LED comes on.

Circuits simplified

Circuit building

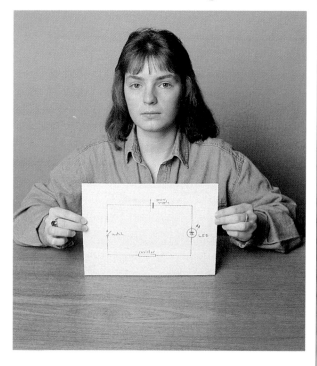

Connect the components together one by one, following the diagram.

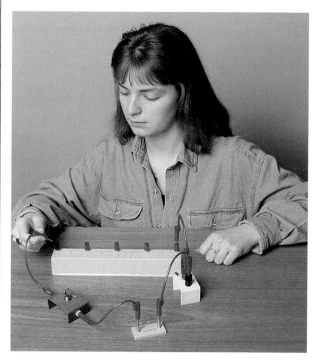

Lay out the components in the same arrangement as in the diagram.

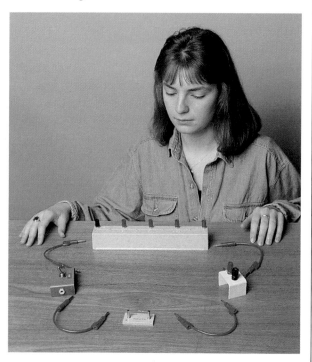

Check that it works.

Components can be soldered onto a circuit board. The result is robust and compact, and it can be very complicated.

Voltage provides push. A voltmeter measures the voltage between any two points in a circuit. Finish building your circuit before you connect a voltmeter – it has to be connected in parallel and it can be confusing.

Circuit testing

A multimeter can measure the resistance of any component. Cover up the LDR and its resistance shoots up.

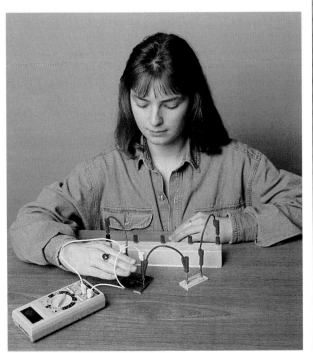

Current is the flow. An ammeter measures the current. The current flows in one lead and out the other.

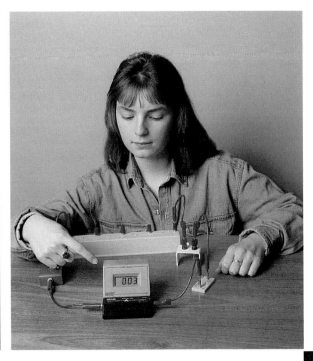

Case study: Fragile new life

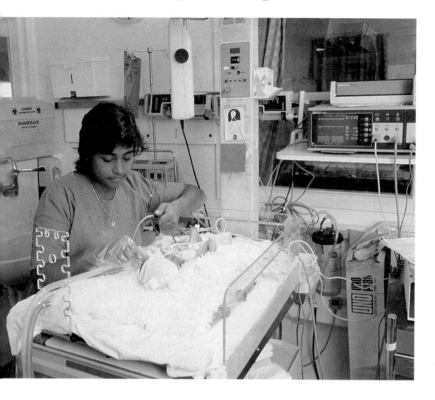

Most babies are born after about 40 weeks of pregnancy, but some arrive early. These premature babies need extra help to get them through the first days of their new lives.

Nurses at St Richard's Hospital in Chichester, Sussex, explain how they combine their skills with modern technology to give a good start in life to very tiny babies.

▲ 'Here in the Special Care Baby Unit we look after premature babies who might heve been born as much as eight weeks early. Without our help, life would be a struggle for them, and many of them wouldn't make it. When a newborn baby comes into the unit we have several checks to do.'

'We need to know the baby's weight. If it has to have medicine then the dose will depend on its weight.' ▶

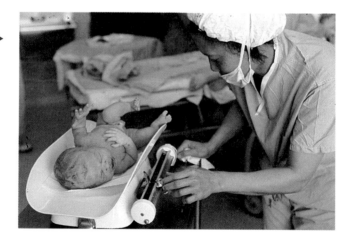

Too much handling can be a shock to such young babies. An incubator provides the right environment at a time when they are very vulnerable. The temperature inside the incubator is carefully controlled.

'A temperature probe on the baby's ▶ skin allows continuous monitoring, and we don't have to disturb the baby. We also measure air temperature around the baby.'

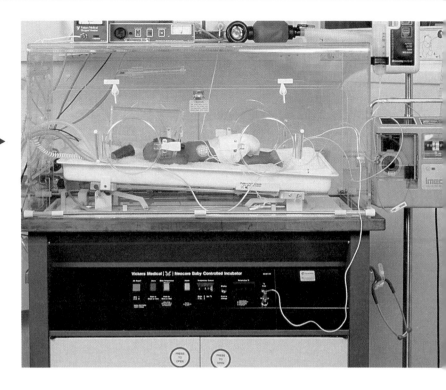

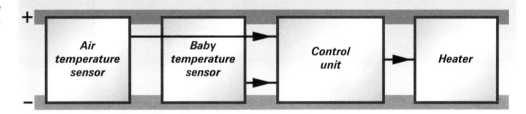

▶ *If the temperature of the baby or the air falls then the heater comes on*

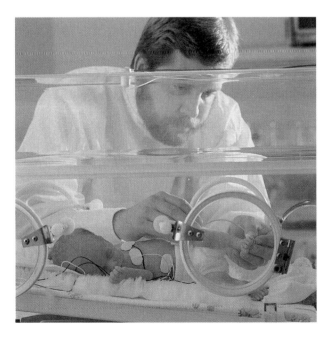

◀ 'The babies are naked except for a nappy. That makes it easy for us to watch their breathing and skin colour. A small probe attached to a baby's foot connects it to the oxygen saturation monitor. If the baby doesn't have enough oxygen in its bloodstream we can supply extra oxygen.'

'Under the sheet is a mattress ▶ like a small airbed. As the baby breathes, the slight movements compress the air in the mattress compartments and a sensor detects movement of air between the compartments. If the baby doesn't breathe for 20 seconds then an alarm sounds.'

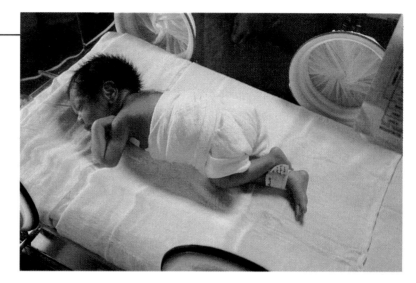

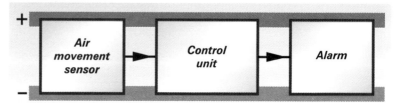

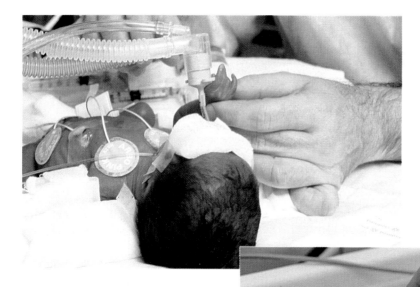

◀ 'Babies with serious lung problems need more help with their breathing. The transcutaneous monitor detects the level of CO_2 in their blood. If it's too high then the ventilator can do their breathing for them.'

'To monitor heart rate we ▶ have an ECG machine – electrocardiograph. We stick three small probes to the baby's skin to detect electrical voltages that are generated in the baby's body with each beat of the heart.'

Every hour the nurses make a detailed record of each baby's condition. The instruments are important, but the nurses' experience and their direct observations are essential.

'A lot of our work involves checking the machines. The oxygen cylinder might need to be changed, or the humidifier might need more water. If the reading on the oxygen level meter in the incubator drops it may be the meter itself that is at fault. We check that it reads 21% in normal air. We use our judgement to set alarm limits to suit each baby's condition.'

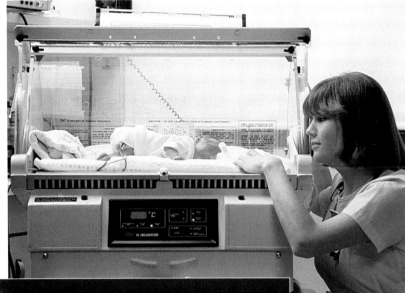

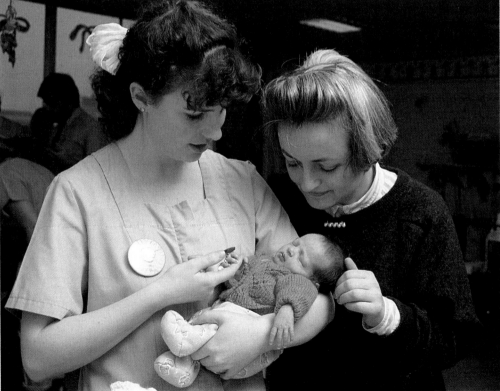

▲ 'Within a few weeks a baby can be fighting fit. In the meantime the baby's parents need support as well. We have a room where mothers can stay to be close to their baby. We explain everything that we're doing, and involve parents as much as we can.'

Electronics – components and circuits

Supply voltage

All parts of an electronic device need to be connected to the supply voltage. There is usually a positive line along the top of the circuitry, connected to the positive terminal of the power supply. The negative line then runs along the bottom.

inputs

LDR

LDR stands for light dependent resistor. An LDR has a resistance of about 10 million ohms (10 MΩ) in the dark, but this falls to about 1000 ohms (1 kΩ) in bright light.

Thermistor

A thermistor is a temperature sensor. It's just a block af material that doesn't conduct very well at room temperature. But when it gets hotter more of its electrons become free to flow and it has less resistance.

Pulse generator

A pulse generator produces very regular bursts of signal, usually at a high frequency. Capacitors and resistors connected to the pulse generator control its frequency.

processor

Comparator

This compares the voltage of two inputs. Its output depends on which input is the higher voltage.

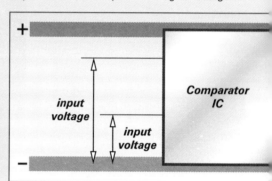

Semiconductor components

Semiconductors are materials like silicon and germanium that don't conduct electricity as well as metals do. Impurities in semiconductor materials make a big difference to how they conduct. Different impurities in different regions in a block of semiconductor make electric current flow easily in some places but not in others.

Diodes are the simplest type of semiconductor component. They allow current to flow through them in one direction only, like electrical one-way valves.

Transistors are like diodes that can be switched on and off by a small voltage (0.6 V) applied to their 'base' connection.

Integrated circuits or 'chips' are small blocks of semiconductor with complex patterns of impurities inside them. These patterns create thousands of tiny transistors. The semiconductor is sealed inside a small plastic package with metal legs to connect it to a circuit.

Signals and logic

A signal is a varying electrical voltage that links one part of an electronic device to the next. The voltage of the signal can vary between a very low voltage ('off') and the supply voltage ('on'). If the voltage doesn't have any inbetween values but jumps between 'on' and 'off' then we say that the signal is digital. 'Off' is called logic state 0 and 'on' is called logic state 1.

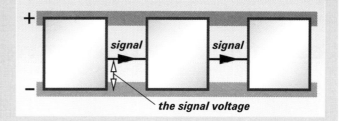

the signal voltage

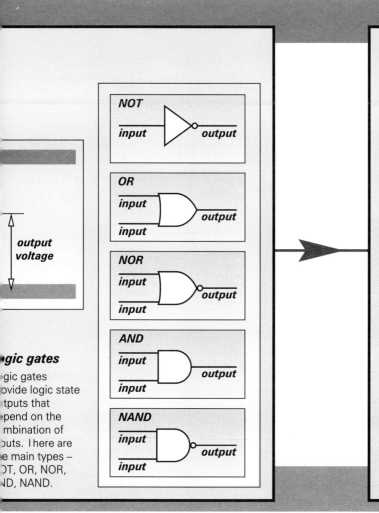

output voltage

NOT

input — output

OR

input
input — output

NOR

input
input — output

AND

input
input — output

NAND

input
input — output

Logic gates

Logic gates provide logic state outputs that depend on the combination of inputs. There are five main types – NOT, OR, NOR, AND, NAND.

outputs

LED

A light emitting diode gives out light and doesn't get hot. It only needs a current of about 0.1 A, so it can be included in an electronic circuit without use of relays or transducer drivers.

Relay

Electronic circuits only provide small currents. These are not big enough to work a lamp, heater or motor. But an electronic circuit can control a magnetic switch, or relay, to switch on the power supply to a separate circuit.

Transducer driver

A transducer driver acts as an electronic relay. A low voltage output from a processor switches on the power supply to a motor, lamp or buzzer.

Motors, lamps and buzzers

These all need relays or transducer drivers when they are controlled by electronic circuits

An example of an electronic device

This device provides control and movement. It senses rain and then switches on the wipers to wipe intermittently.

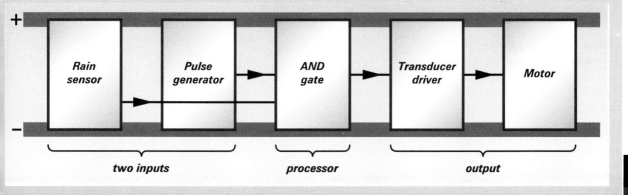

two inputs   processor   output

Case study: Computer rescue

▲ *Off to rescue another driver stuck with a broken-down car*

The RAC provides a rescue service to people when their cars break down. RAC patrol vans carry all the right tools so that the patrol officer can fix most problems on the roadside. The whole of their national network depends on careful co-ordination of resources. Computers play a big part in the organisation.

'The computer network has a database which keeps a record of all the calls we ever get and then analyses them,' says Andrew Scotford, Commercial Training Manager with the RAC. 'That tells us where and when the demand is greatest, during the day, the week and the year, so we can work out the best shift pattern for the patrols, and we can plan their training. We want enough patrols available to deal with incidents within our target times. But we don't want so many out there that some have got nothing to do.'

Mark Saunders and Alan Frost, GNVQ students at Darlaston Community School near Birmingham, spent two weeks on work experience at the RAC Regional Supercentre which controls the patrols and takes breakdown calls.

▲ *Mark Saunders receiving calls from people in distress*

'I did an assignment about the use of computers to control phone calls,' says Mark. 'I spent a morning on the telephones, taking calls for help from people who'd broken down. I was sat there wearing my headset and I had to type all the details into the computer. I followed the call through till it got to the patrol.'

The RAC aims to answer all calls within 10 seconds. The Birmingham Supercentre covers a big area, the whole of Wales and then as far as Norwich in the east, but the call goes to whichever command centre is the first one available. 'We take calls here and send vehicles to help people,' says Andrew Scotford. 'That involves our computer linking with terminals on board all the vehicles in our area.'

'We need to know about traffic jams so that we can provide our members with the best possible service,' he continues. 'The information helps the people in the Supercentre to make the right decision about sending patrol vans to breakdowns. To help them they have a computer display system called 'Graphic Dispatch'. A map on the screen shows the positions of the patrol vans and the reported breakdown. The dispatchers then decide how to deal with the incident. They decide which patrol to send. If no RAC patrol is available, they will choose to send an independent garage contractor.'

▲ *Alan Frost's work experience results in another grateful driver*

'I spent two days on the road in the Wolverhampton area. I learnt about electronic ignition systems here one day,' says Alan Frost. 'Then the next day I was out on the road trying to get somebody's car started. I had to use what I'd learnt, and it worked. Now all vans are getting CD ROMs so that all sorts of information on faults on cars will be instantly available in the van.

'Electronic ignition systems in cars use an electronic control unit, ECU, which receives information from a range of sensors such as airflow meters, engine-speed sensors and temperature sensors,' Alan explains. 'The ECU controls ignition by controlling outputs to the fuel pump, fuel injectors and ignition coil. These deliver fuel to the engine and provide the voltage to give the spark at the spark plugs. If the information from the sensors changes then the ECU changes these outputs. For instance, a cold engine needs more fuel than a warm engine.'

▼ *The main parts of an electronic ignition system*

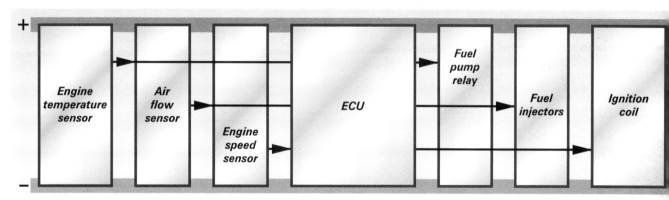

'On the car that I fixed the temperature sensor had failed and the ECU was working as if the engine was cold, but it wasn't. It was flooding the engine with fuel. We used a voltmeter to check all the sensors and outputs to find out which one wasn't working. The van was carrying a spare, so we were able to get the driver straight back onto the road.'

THOUGHTS AND ACTIONS

1 Trains that use Hugh Barton's emergency lamp (see 'Light work') have a reduced speed limit. They must be visible by someone who is 25 s further down the line. The speed limit is set so that this is not more than 800 m away.
   a Use speed = distance /time to work out the speed in ms^{-1} of a train travelling at this speed limit.
   b What is this speed in $km\,s^{-1}$?
   c What is it in $km\,hour^{-1}$?
   d A train is scheduled to take half an hour to travel between two stations, 60 km apart. What is the shortest time that the train will take if it is lit by an emergency lamp and has the maximum speed worked out in part (c)?
   e The train will take longer than this? Why?

2 Look at Hugh Barton's 'low battery warning' circuit. The supply voltage is normally 12 V.
   a If voltage V_2 is always 6 V, what is the voltage across resistor R_2 at full supply voltage?
   b What will the voltage across R_2 be if the supply voltage falls to 11 V?
   c If V_1 is 6.2 V at full supply voltage what is the voltage across R_1?

3 Hugh Barton made many tests and then developed a 'specification' that the manufacturer could use to build large numbers of the lamp. Imagine that you are the manufacturer of tropical fish tanks. Several suppliers have offered to make 12 V, 5 W thermostatic heaters for your tanks. Write a detailed specification for their designers to work to. You could mention:

   electrical requirements, size and portability, safety requirements, range of temperatures, reliability, sensitivity, cost.

4 Read 'Fragile new life'. Sketch an electronic system for either,
   a setting off an alarm if the power supply fails to the monitoring circuits of a baby in an incubator. What sort of alarm would be suitable?
   b or setting off an alarm if the baby's nappy becomes wet. What kind of alarm would be suitable for a baby in a special care unit?

5 Draw a flow chart to show the sequence of events that takes place when a motorist in trouble telephones the RAC.

6 Explain how information technology improves:
   a the efficiency of a person who works at the RAC responding to 'phone calls from motorists,
   b the efficiency of an RAC patrol officer.

7 The ECU in an electronic ignition system runs off a 12 V power supply. At the RAC, Alan Frost used a voltmeter to check which of the inputs and outputs of the system wasn't working.
   Set up an electronic system with an appropriate power supply, one or more inputs, a processor, and one or more outputs. This will act as a model of the electronic ignition system.
   a Draw a diagram of the system and measure and record the voltages across the different components when it is working properly.
   b Find out what a voltmeter reads when one of the inputs or outputs is broken so that there is no current through it. (There is no need to break the inputs or outputs! Make them behave as if they were broken.)

8 Use page 180 of the 'Reference section' and choose five commonly used electrical symbols, including a power source. Create a display, on a poster or computer screen, that will help students to remember these symbols. On your display include a complete circuit of all the five components – say what the circuit does and what is the purpose of the five components.

9 Connect up a circuit which includes an LDR and an ammeter. Place a large beaker so that it is in a stable position, upright, covering the LDR. Pour a dark or cloudy liquid into the beaker and measure the current at different depths of the liquid.
   a Plot a graph of your results.
   b What possible commercial applications does this circuit have?
   c Sketch an electronic system, based on this circuit, that sets off an alarm when the liquid reaches a certain depth.
   d How could you adapt such a warning system so that it works with clear water? When could this be useful?

Monitoring human performance

Reasons for monitoring performance

Methods of monitoring

The effect of different conditions on performance

Targets

After working through this element you should:

- have prepared a report on monitoring a physical task under different conditions. Your report should show that you know which conditions can change performance and that you can describe the best conditions for completeing the task
- have selected a suitable physical task involving moving or lifting
- have monitored speed, strength, stamina, reaction time and recovery rate
- have monitored the effect of the following conditions: load being carried, fitness level in different people, different mental conditions such as confidence and stress
- be able to give examples of how monitoring helps in: recovery from injury, learning new physical skills, strengthening muscles and improving posture
- be able to explain how the demands of the body for food and oxygen increase during exercise, and how these demands are met
- be able to explain the increased amounts of waste products produced by the body during exercise and how these waste products are removed
- know that familiarity with the task, oxygen supply, fatigue and level of skill can all affect performance
- be aware of the safety measures which should be observed when asking volunteers to undergo physical fitness testing.

Cross references

The following pages in this book will also help you to achieve these targets:

30 Photosynthesis and nutrition

39 Chicken for dinner

140 Tension that heals

178 Human biology

Key words

Some of the technical words for this element are listed in the targets. These are some more: circulation, cardiovascular, metabolism, respiration, haemoglobin, red blood cells, glucose, carbohydrate, amino acid, protein, waste products, excretion, gaseous exchange, vertebrae.

Case study: **Higher, further, faster**

Michael Clarke is an 18-year-old student with a big ambition. He hopes to compete in the Olympic Games as a member of the Men's Gymnastic team.

'A lot of preparation goes into every training session,' says Michael. 'Not only do you need to be physically fit to perform well in gymnastics, you also need a knowledge of anatomy, physiology and even some physics if you are to understand what is happening to your body as you perform.'

A gymnast needs to develop suppleness, strength, stamina and control. Training must include stretching exercises, ballet and dance, attention to posture and the development of spacial awareness. To reach and maintain his present level of fitness and skill Michael trains almost every day of the week. He knows that sporting excellence is a complex business.

The search for perfection

Most of us simply want to be fit enough to be healthy and carry on our normal lives without running out of breath. But some people take the quest for fitness much, much further than this. They want to be the fastest, leap the highest, be the strongest or most supple.

When you were a baby beginning to walk, every step was a triumph of balance and co-ordination over gravity. As your body has become familiar with the task, your muscles have developed, the movements have become smooth and you no longer think about putting one foot in front of the other. In the same way an athlete or gymnast will learn a new skill. They train so that it becomes a smooth, polished movement which does not reveal the effort that has gone into achieving that perfection.

Exercise and fitness

Fitness involves stamina and suppleness. Stamina is your abilty to keep going and suppleness is your abilty to move your joints easily and fully. It also involves strength.

A simple approach to measuring fitness is to use your pulse rate to measure how quickly your heart is beating. Your heart is made of muscle which grows larger with regular exercise – and a fit heart pumps very efficiently. A low resting pulse rate and only a small increase in the pulse rate after exercise indicate fitness.

Regular exercise keeps your body working as efficiently as possible. It does this by improving the circulation of the blood, improving your overall muscle tone and by raising the 'metabolic rate' so that food is used up more quickly and energy is quickly available to the muscles.

Different types of exercise improve fitness in different ways as this table shows.

EXERCISE	AVERAGE ENERGY EXPENDITURE /kJ min^{-1}	STAMINA	SUPPLENESS	STRENGTH
Golf	10–20	poor	fair	poor
Walking slowly		fair	poor	poor
Tennis	21–30	fair	good	fair
Gymnastics		fair	excellent	good
Jogging		excellent	fair	fair
Cycling slowly		good	fair	good
Walking quickly		good	poor	poor
Football	over 30	good	good	good
Swimming		excellent	excellent	excellent
Squash		excellent	good	fair
Cycling fast		excellent	fair	good
Disco dancing		good	excellent	poor

In exercise laboratories the rate of taking in oxygen or producing carbon dioxide can be measured whilst someone exercises on a treadmill going at different speeds. The chemical make-up of the blood and even the events within the muscles themselves can be measured to give a full picture of fitness.

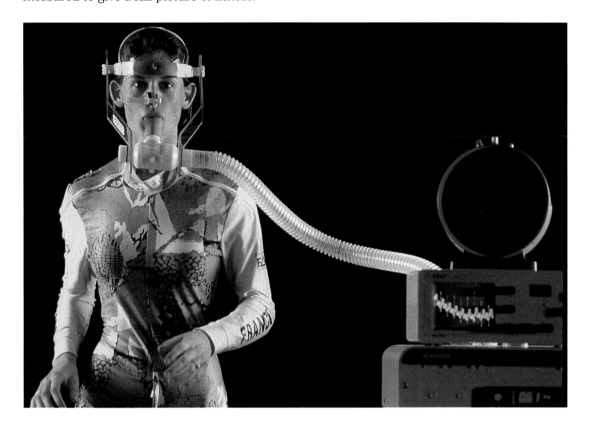

Skill in any physical activity is learned – it results from experience and needs practice. Anyone can produce a one off 'fluke' in sport – but it takes endless practice to be able to do it every time.

CHARACTERISTICS OF PERFORMANCE	NOVICE	EXPERT
Speed	Slow, poorly synchronized	Task paced, fast if necessary
Errors	Many of almost any kind	Few; tend to occur with specific movements
Observable quality	Clumsy, jerky, exaggerated or excessive movement	Smooth, integrated
Attention	Every movement monitored	Occasional monitoring
Fatigue	Occurs rapidly	Minimal fatigue

Eating and drinking Food provides the raw materials for building muscles and other body tissues' as well as an energy supply. Water is the medium for all the chemical reactions of the body and we also need it for the removal of waste.

Inhalation We breathe in air made up mostly of nitrogen and oxygen. We need the oxygen for the transfer of energy in the cells. When the level of physical activity increases the rate and depth of inhalation must increase to bring more oxygen into the body.

Digestion The gut or digestive system is basically a long muscular tube running through the body. It breaks down the food we eat into much smaller molecules which can pass into our blood to be used by the body as fuel or building blocks. Glucose from carbohydrates is particularly important as fuel, whilst amino acids from proteins are used for the formation of new cells.

Circulation A transport system is necessary to carry the food and oxygen rich blood to the tissues and to remove the waste products of cell respiration before they poison the system. The blood vessels form a network of transport vessels to and from every area of the body, whilst the blood carries the chemicals.

The heart acts as a pump to force the blood around the system. It is a double pump – blood is forced to the lungs to pick up oxygen and then returned to the heart from where it is pumped out again to travel all round the body.

Cellular respiration Within each of our body cells, hundreds of chemical reactions take place. The name for all of these reactions is our 'metabolism'.

Most of these reactions need an energy supply, which comes from the breakdown of glucose in the presence of oxygen in a complex process called respiration. A simplified summary of respiration is:

$$\text{glucose} + \text{oxygen} \longrightarrow \text{carbon dioxide} + \text{water} + \text{energy transfer}$$

If there is not enough oxygen present then the glucose cannot be broken down properly. Less energy is available and lactic acid is formed instead of carbon dioxide and water. The lactic acid stops the muscles working properly and that is why performance is so closely related to the ability to get oxygen efficiently into the body.

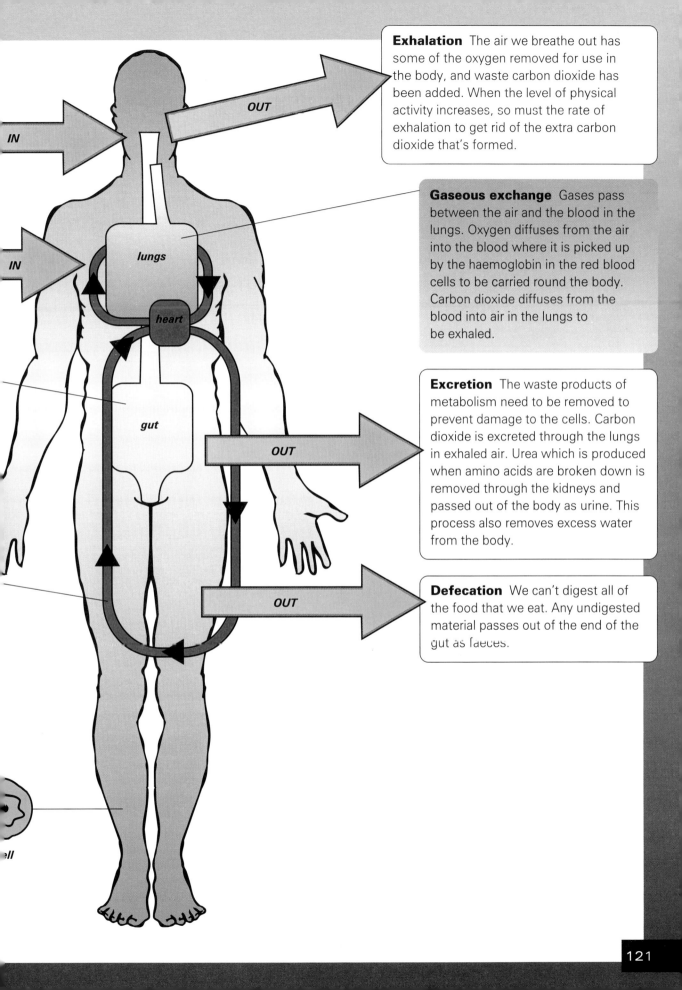

IN

OUT

IN

lungs

heart

gut

OUT

OUT

Exhalation The air we breathe out has some of the oxygen removed for use in the body, and waste carbon dioxide has been added. When the level of physical activity increases, so must the rate of exhalation to get rid of the extra carbon dioxide that's formed.

Gaseous exchange Gases pass between the air and the blood in the lungs. Oxygen diffuses from the air into the blood where it is picked up by the haemoglobin in the red blood cells to be carried round the body. Carbon dioxide diffuses from the blood into air in the lungs to be exhaled.

Excretion The waste products of metabolism need to be removed to prevent damage to the cells. Carbon dioxide is excreted through the lungs in exhaled air. Urea which is produced when amino acids are broken down is removed through the kidneys and passed out of the body as urine. This process also removes excess water from the body.

Defecation We can't digest all of the food that we eat. Any undigested material passes out of the end of the gut as faeces.

ll

121

Case study: **A pain in the neck**

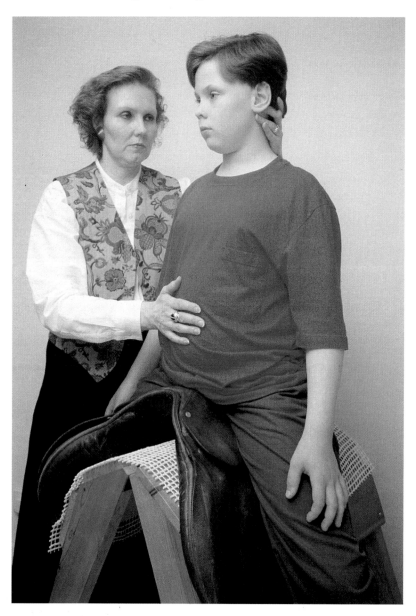

◀ *Kathryn Sandiforth teaches the Alexander Technique*

Widget Software Ltd produces software and peripherals for hand-held computers. They've had a few problems – not with their computer products but with the spines of their staff. Linda Brown, one of the employees, developed a bad neck from straining to look at her computer monitor and problems with her back and hips as she lifted parcels and bent to filing cabinets. Mark Needham, the managing director of Widget, also developed a pain in the back from sitting slumped for hours over a computer. To try and overcome these difficulties Widget brought in Kathryn Sandiforth, a qualified teacher of the Alexander Technique.

The Alexander Technique is concerned with the mechanics of body balance and our control over them.

As you go about your everyday activities you are usually completely unaware of the work that your spine is doing. Try lifting someone of comparable size to yourself – your skeleton and muscles are supporting that sort of mass against gravity all the time. Your head alone is an extremely heavy burden to carry, particularly balanced as it is on a small joint at the top of the neck.

And the small bones or vertebrae which make up our backbone don't just provide support. They also protect the body's main nervous highway, the spinal nerves which carry nerve impulses to and from our brains.

Back pain is a big issue – and to those who suffer it really hurts. In any two week period 80% of adults in the UK suffer from some degree of back pain. Once the back is damaged, the performance of the whole body is affected. Try looking around the room without moving your neck as a simple example of how spinal problems can interfere with everyday life.

For many people the pain in their back is at least partly self-inflicted. Poor posture and lifting heavy items without bending the knees contribute to many back problems. In a correct lift the load is taken more equally between the thighs and the back. The spine takes too much of the strain when we don't do it right.

One of the more serious back problems is a slipped disc. The spongy cartilage discs between the vertebrae act as shock absorbers. If the strain on the back is too great the disc doesn't actually slip – it bulges. If it presses on one of the spinal nerves it will cause a lot of pain.

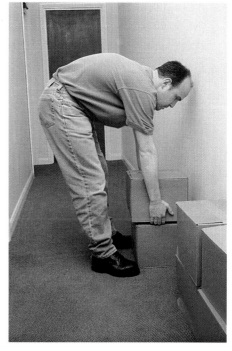

▲ *Wrong*

▲ *Wrong*

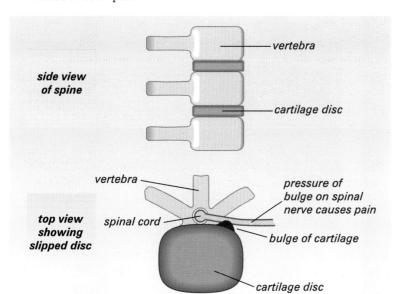

side view of spine

vertebra

cartilage disc

top view showing slipped disc

vertebra

spinal cord

pressure of bulge on spinal nerve causes pain

bulge of cartilage

cartilage disc

Slipped discs in the upper spine or whip-lash injuries from car accidents may be helped by special supporting collars which take the strain off the spine in the neck region.

When all else fails, some spinal problems can ▶ be solved by surgery. This may involve removing the bulging part of a damaged disc or inserting rods to fuse areas of the spine together to adjust the curvature of the spine.

If back problems are caused by distortions in the shape of the spine or by misaligned bones then help may be gained from special massages, exercises and manipulation by physiotherapists, chiropractors and osteopaths. ▼

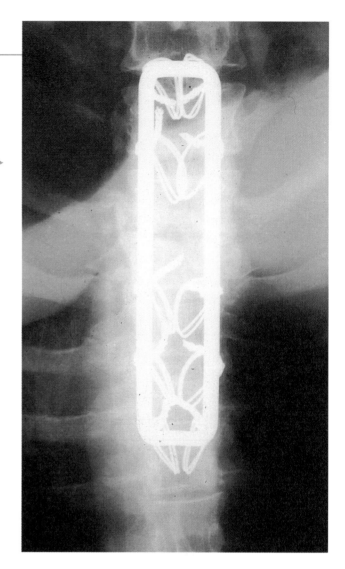

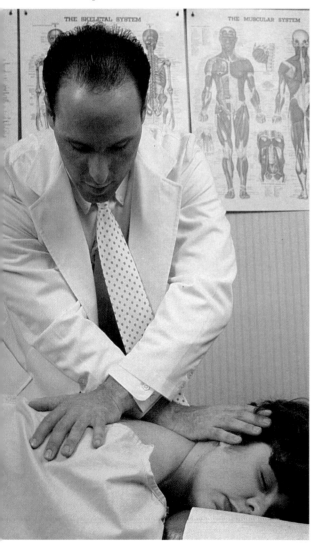

Acupuncture is very effective in the treatment of back pain. ▼

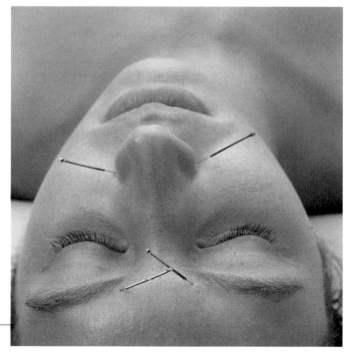

Therapies such as the Alexander Technique deal with the cause of back pain. By helping people to change their posture they bring relief from discomfort and give enhanced body performance.

▲ *Right*

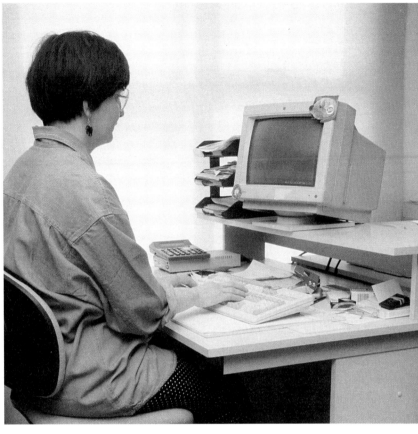

▲ *Right*

Bad posture can lead to hunching, compression of the ribs and less effective breathing. The Alexander Technique teaches people to balance their heads correctly on their necks, and to be aware of the way they use their body in all daily activities. This means they can use the curvature of their spine properly and so avoid stress, damage and pain.

Using the awareness that Kathryn taught them to protect their backs and minimize the muscular effort used during the day, the Widget staff are now free from back pain. They can perform both their workplace tasks and their home activities more effectively and painlessly.

1 a Read 'Higher, further, faster'. What aspects of fitness are particularly important to gymnasts like Michael Clarke? What sort of training programme should he follow to develop and maintain the right fitness?

   b What aspect of fitness is most important to:
(i) a sprinter
(ii) a long distance runner
(iii) a car rally driver?

2 Record your pulse rate. If you are healthy then do ⚠ step-ups steadily, not too hard, for 3 minutes, and record your pulse again straight away.
Obtain similar data for as many other people as possible.

   a Present your results graphically.

   b Record the mean, median and mode of your results.

   c Find out how long it takes for your pulse rate to return to its resting rate after you finish doing step-ups.

   d Does added load, such as ankle weights or a heavy book, make any difference to pulse rate at the end of three minutes or to recovery time?

3 Three different people go to a leisure centre to improve their fitness:
• Jenny is an 18-year-old who has recently left full-time education. She has always played a lot of sport – hockey, tennis and swimming. After three months at work she doesn't want to lose her fitness.
• Steve is a 19-year-old couch potato. He was unemployed for a year and now has an office job. He has spent most of his time either drinking pints in his local pub or watching TV. His girlfriend has teased him about getting fat, and he wants to improve his fitness.
• Mahmood is recovering from a torn calf muscle, injured while playing cricket. He is normally fit but his physiotherapist told him not to exercise heavily for six weeks in case he damaged the weakened muscle again. Now he wants to get back to playing cricket as quickly as possible.

   a How could staff at a health suite assess the fitness of these people?

   b What sort of programme would be suitable for them?

   c What sort of safety precautions should they follow?

   d How could you monitor Steve's progress?

4 a Which of the processes shown in 'Digestion, circulation and respiration' speed up during exercise?

   b The arrows showing inputs and outputs are not shown to scale. Create sketches, with arrows drawn to scale, to demonstrate your answer to part a).

5 a Compare respiration with photosynthesis.

   b Respiration takes place in cells. Draw the inputs and outputs for an individual cell.

6 Read 'A pain in the neck'. If you were the Managing Director of an electronics company, would you spend money on posture training for your staff? Justify your answer.

7 The Alexander Technique is concerned with the ⚠ head.

   a Assume the mass of an adult human head is 5 kg.

   b Devise a way of measuring the volume of a head (without detaching it!). Record your result.

   c Use density = mass /volume, and assume that the mass is 5 kg, to calculate the density of the head.

   d Do you think that density of a head is related to mental abilities?

8 Devise a simple test to monitor the powers of concentration of individuals. Use the test to find out about factors which might affect concentration, such as age or the presence of distractions. Present your findings with the data clearly displayed in the form of a brief paper to be delivered to a scientific meeting.

9 Look at page 178 of the 'Reference section'. Which of the six body systems is concerned with,

   a fuel and nutrient inputs

   b gaseous exchange

   c body structure and posture

   d sensing information from surroundings and coordinating movement

   e waste material output

   f internal transport of dissolved materials.

Monitoring and controlling chemical reactions

Measuring rates of reaction

Varying conditions to control rate of reaction

The particle explanations of why rates of reaction change

Targets

After working through this element you should:

- have prepared a report on one chemical reaction that you have monitored and controlled
- have explained why it's necessary to control the rate of the chemical reaction
- have chosen the most suitable method for monitoring rate of reaction, which could involve measurement of rate of formation of product, consumption of reactant, colour change, rate of bubbling, temperature change, or pH change
- have investigated the conditions which influence the rate of reaction, including concentration of reactants, temperature, surface area and the presence of a catalyst
- have controlled the conditions to make sure that the rate of reaction is safe
- have controlled conditions to make sure that reactants are used up at a manageable rate and products are produced at a manageable rate
- have controlled conditions to make sure that energy transfer to and from the reaction is manageable and safe
- be able to give examples of control of reaction rates in commercial production processes
- be aware of some of the problems involved in large scale production of chemicals
- be able to use models of atoms, molecules and ions to explain how altering conditions, concentration, temperature and surface area affects reaction rate.

Key words

Some of the technical words for this element are listed in the targets. These are some more: effervescence, endothermic, exothermic.

Case study: **Precious metals**

◀ *Crystalline silver is made using a process that's about 150 years old.*

You can see why you are liable to be scanned with a metal detector when you visit the Johnson Matthey factory. Gold, silver, platinum, rhodium and other precious metals are their raw materials. Rhodium is really precious – anything from £15 000 to £100 000 per kilogram, depending on the market. These expensive metals and their compounds are used to make anything from anti-cancer drugs to electronic components.

'One of our major products goes to the photographic industry,' says Peter Skinner, a chemical consultant. Photographic film manufacturers use silver nitrate to make photosensitive film. The raw materials are simple; silver and concentrated nitric acid. But you can't just add them together. You have to control the process at every stage. If the reaction gets out of hand, acid splashing occurs and a toxic gas is produced at a rate that's difficult to cope with.

The main reaction in making silver nitrate:

silver + nitric acid ⟶ silver nitrate + nitrogen dioxide + water

$$Ag + 2HNO_3 \longrightarrow AgNO_3 + NO_2 + H_2O$$

'We use crystalline silver,' Peter says. 'Silver powder, that's anything less than a millimetre in diameter, would react far too quickly. Whoosh and it would be gone. We would have to cool the reactor or there'd be too much gas production and spitting and splashing of acid. Using silver bars has problems too. At first the acid would etch the bars and there would be hardly any reaction at all. Crystalline silver, between 1 and 6 mm in diameter, has a modest surface area that allows the reaction to proceed at a steady rate. It's fed into the nitric acid automatically at normal temperature and, as it's an exothermic reaction, it heats itself up to 100–120 °C.'

The newly made silver nitrate solution collects in a holding tank. Brown nitrogen dioxide gas moves into a scrubbing tower at the top of the reactor where it's mixed with oxygen. Water trickles down the packing in the tower, reacting with the upward moving mixture of gases. The packing provides a large surface area, giving the maximum contact of water with the gases.

Recycling nitrogen dioxide in the scrubbing tower:

nitrogen dioxide + water + oxygen ⟶ nitric acid

$$4NO_2 + 2H_2O + O_2 \longrightarrow 4HNO_3$$

'The nitric acid produced goes back into the reaction,' Peter explains. 'We have the cost of the oxygen, of course, but we also solve the environmental problem of getting rid of harmful nitrogen dioxide.'

'The controlling factor in this reaction is the amount of concentrated nitric acid. An automatic gauge controls the amount of concentrated acid added. After a while the acid in the reactor gets diluted by returning acid from the tower. We monitor the temperature, and if it drops it's a sign that concentrated acid is needed more quickly. If the temperature rises then the amount added is cut back.'

'At the end of a run,' Peter continues, 'we stop the reaction either by cutting off the acid flow or the silver feed. The main reason for stopping the flow every so often is to recover the valuable gold that collects as an impurity at the bottom of the vessel.'

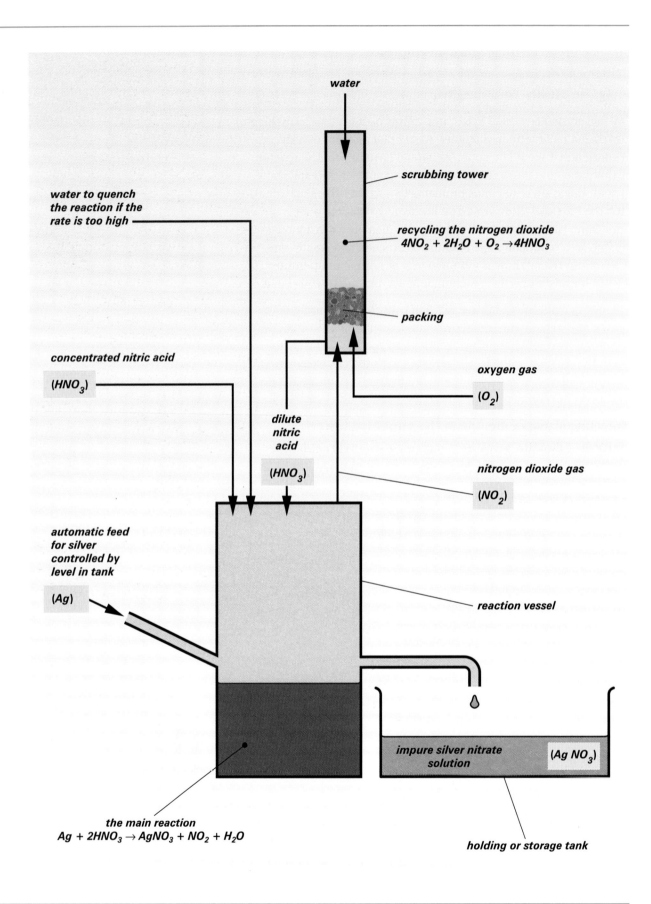

water

scrubbing tower

water to quench
the reaction if the
rate is too high

recycling the nitrogen dioxide
$4NO_2 + 2H_2O + O_2 \rightarrow 4HNO_3$

packing

concentrated nitric acid

(HNO$_3$)

oxygen gas

(O$_2$)

dilute
nitric
acid

(HNO$_3$)

nitrogen dioxide gas

(NO$_2$)

automatic feed
for silver
controlled by
level in tank

(Ag)

reaction vessel

impure silver nitrate
solution

(Ag NO$_3$)

the main reaction
$Ag + 2HNO_3 \rightarrow AgNO_3 + NO_2 + H_2O$

holding or storage tank

▶ *Cooling slowly gives plate-like crystals of silver nitrate*

Pure silver nitrate solution is colourless. The pale green solution in the storage tank contains silver nitrate with some iron and copper and also some unused nitric acid, impurities that must be removed. Peter explains how it's done: 'We neutralize the unwanted acid by adding excess pure moist silver oxide and then, as the pH rises from about 2 to 6, copper and iron react to form insoluble hydroxides so we can filter them off.'

Getting rid of leftover acid:

$$\text{silver oxide} + \text{nitric acid} \longrightarrow \text{silver nitrate} + \text{water}$$
$$Ag_2O \quad + \quad 2HNO_3 \quad \longrightarrow \quad 2AgNO_3 \quad + \quad H_2O$$

The solution is evaporated and cooled a number of times to give fine crystals of silver nitrate. The crystals are then dried. 'Our yield is very high, nearly 100%,' says Peter. 'We're dealing with precious metal chemicals and nothing is thrown away. Even the rags and filter cloths used in the process are burned to recover small amounts of silver. And our product is so pure that to produce photographic film that gives special effects "impurities", such as gold, are added back again. '

Silver nitrate is a commodity product. It's the key substance used to make nearly all other products containing silver. Several thousand tonnes a year are used to make photographic film. It's used to make the silver potassium cyanide for silver plating, to make the silver oxide for use in watch batteries, and to make silver chloride used to 'seed' clouds to encourage rain. Perhaps that's how clouds get their silver linings.

Collisions count

At home and in industry people try to make chemical reactions happen more quickly or more slowly by changing temperature, concentration, pressure or the surface area of the materials involved. Using catalysts is another way of increasing reaction rate.

Chemical reactions involve bond breaking and bond making. Reactions can happen if particles collide with one another with enough energy to start bond breaking. Once bonds are broken atoms can react by rearranging to make new substances. Simple models of atoms, ions and molecules help us to understand how rates of reaction can change.

Temperature...

At home people use appliances like the ones in this showroom to alter the rate at which chemical changes happen to food by varying temperature.

◀ **Low temperature, slow particles, few collisions**

▶ **Higher temperature, faster particles, more collisions and harder collisions**

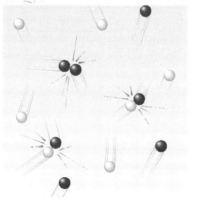

Pressure...

Increasing the pressure on gases pushes the molecules closer together. They bang against one another more often. This means that reactions between gases are often faster when pressure is increased. To make fertilizer, chemists react together hydrogen and nitrogen gases under conditions of increased temperature and pressure and using a catalyst. Under normal conditions these gases hardly react at all.

▶ **Low pressure gas, particles far apart, few collisions**

▲ **For gases, increasing the pressure decreases the volume. The particles are closer together so there are more collisions. The effect is the same as increasing the concentration**

Concentration...

The rate of photosynthesis in green plants can be increased by increasing the concentration of carbon dioxide in the air.

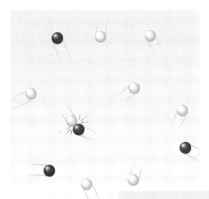

◄ Low concentration, few collisions

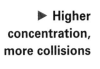

► Higher concentration, more collisions

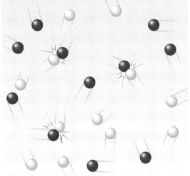

Surface area...

The surfaces of limestone buildings and statues crumble away when exposed to acid rain. Notice that parts like noses with the largest surface areas corrode away fastest.

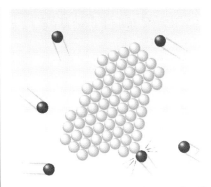

◄ Small surface area – less opportunity for collisions

► Bigger surface area – more collisions between reacting particles.

Catalysts...

Many industrial processes use catalysts to speed up reactions. Catalysts aren't used up in the reaction and so can be used over and over again. A section containing a catalyst can be fitted to car exhausts. This speeds up the rate of conversion of polluting gases into less harmful ones like carbon dioxide.

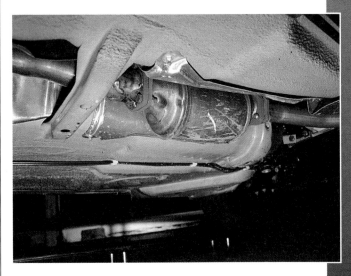

How can you tell how quickly a reaction is going?

You can follow the rate of a chemical reaction by following how much of a new substance is made or how much of one of the starting materials is left. You can also monitor rate throughout a reaction by measuring changes such as colour, pH or volume as they occur. These pages show some practical methods for use in the lab.

Collecting and measuring a gas

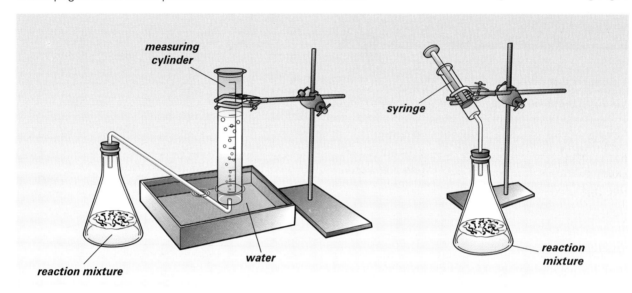

measuring cylinder

reaction mixture

water

syringe

reaction mixture

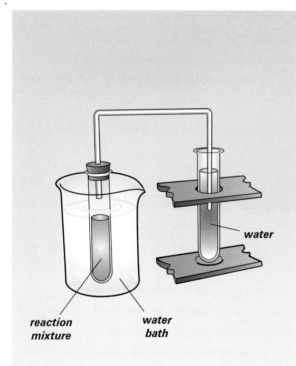

water

reaction mixture

water bath

Counting the bubbling rate

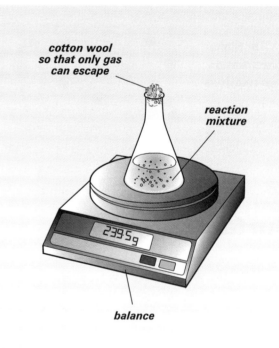

cotton wool so that only gas can escape

reaction mixture

239.5g

balance

Measuring rate of loss of mass when a gas is formed

Timing how long it takes for a solution to turn cloudy

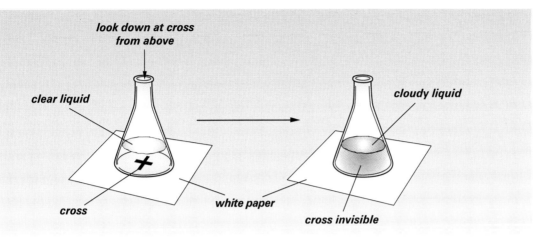

look down at cross from above

clear liquid

cloudy liquid

cross

white paper

cross invisible

For a reaction that produces a cloudy solution you can also take readings from an electric meter. (With the use of a colour filter you can use this method to obtain readings as a colour change takes place.)

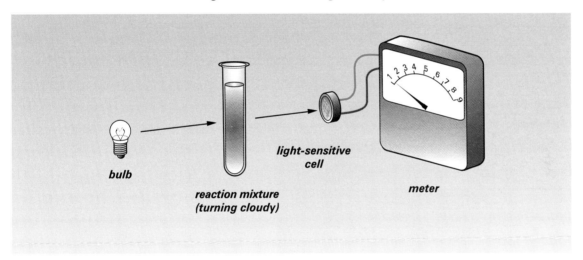

bulb

reaction mixture (turning cloudy)

light-sensitive cell

meter

Measuring the time for a solid to dissolve

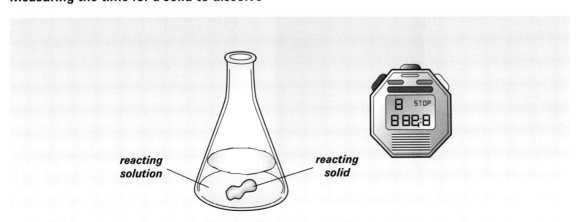

reacting solution

reacting solid

STOP

Case study: Slow reactions in the right packaging

The chemicals in medicines react in the same ways as other chemicals. Stored over time they can react due to light, and react with air or water. The new substances from these reactions do not usually provide effective medical treatment and could be unsafe. Pharmaceutical products are packed and stored in ways chosen to slow down the rate at which these changes take place. The aim is to increase their shelf lives.

Simon Holland is a Team Leader in Pharmaceutical Development at the international drugs company SmithKline Beecham. 'We aim to use packaging that gives our formations a shelf life of 2–3 years with a minimum of 18 months at 25 °C,' he says.

▼ *Unpackaged antibiotic injection has a short shelf-life, but refrigeration makes a big difference*

PRODUCT	SOLUTION USED TO MAKE UP THE INJECTION	VOLUME OF SOLUTION/cm^3	SHELF LIFE AT 25 °C	5 °C
antibiotic injection	water	20	20 mins	
	water	120	4 hours	8 hours
	saline (salt solution)	20	20 mins	
	saline	120	4 hours	8 hours

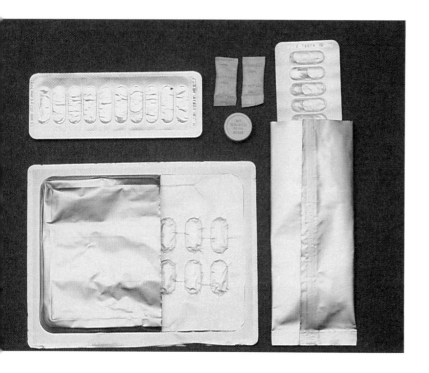

Aluminium/PVC blister packs offer least protection to the entry of moisture – a factor which is particularly important for penicillin products. A blister pack in foil offers better protection. Once opened, the tablets have a shelf life of several weeks which is sufficient for the completion of the course of treatment.

The choice of packaging has to match the local environment where the product will be stored. In hot and humid places like Singapore the blister pack is enclosed in an aluminium pouch containing a desiccant (a drying agent).

Drug products are tested at a wide range of temperature and humidity and for different lengths of time. In a series of rooms the company keeps shelves of drug products all clearly labelled, with some going back five years. Temperatures in the different rooms vary from 5 °C to a very hot 40 °C. The conditions are chosen to match the regulations in different countries.

'After storing a sample of a drug in constant conditions we test it for quality,' Simon explains. 'Do we have 100% of what we started with and if not where has the loss gone? What reaction has taken place and what degradation products are now present?'

Packaging and storage of drugs isn't just about convenience or even just about hygiene. It's about making reaction rates as slow as possible. 'Of course,' says Simon, 'we have no control once our products get to the person who takes the tablets. Just think of the steam in your bathroom – people often have medicine cabinets on the wall.'

▼ *Debbie Hyde in one of the rooms where they test the shelf lives of drugs in different conditions. Readings of temperature and humidity are taken every two minutes night and day at 6 points in the room*

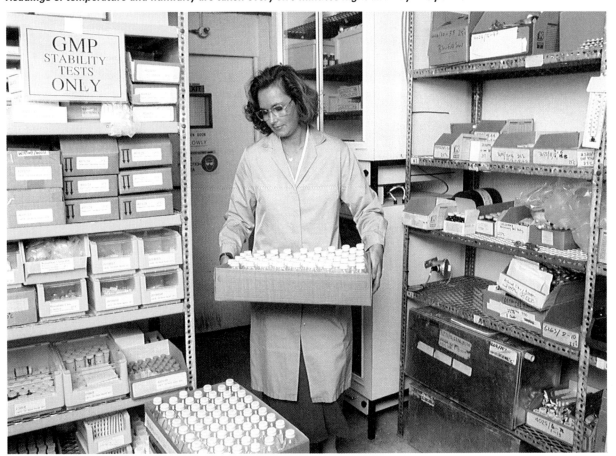

1 **a** Construct a flow diagram to represent the process used to manufacture pure silver nitrate at Johnson Matthey Chemicals.

b What is the toxic gas that's produced by the main reaction?

c Reaction rates in two parts of the process are controlled by surface area. Explain what is done, and how it affects reaction rate.

d Suggest one way in which the company could monitor the rate of the main reaction.

2 **a** Use a suppliers catalogue to find out the cost of a bottle of silver nitrate solution.

b What is the volume of the full bottle of solution?

c What is the molarity of the solution?

d What is the relative formula mass of silver nitrate?

e What is the mass of silver nitrate in a full bottle?

f What is the mass of silver in a full bottle?

g Silver costs about £128 per kilogram, depending on the market. At this price, what is the value of the silver in the bottle?

h Find out why the value of silver fluctuates.

3 **a** How would you monitor the rate of the following reactions:
(i) indigestion (antacid) tablet dissolving?
(ii) indigestion (antacid) tablet neutralising an acid?
(iii) erosion of building material due to acid rain?
(iv) food, such as milk, going 'off'?
(v) yeast respiring?

⚠ **b** Choose one of these reactions, carry out a monitoring exercise, and write a report.

4 Work out the theoretical yield of silver nitrate expected from 100 tonnes of silver by the main reaction used by Johnson Matthey. What special steps do they take to make sure that the actual yield almost matches this?

5 In living things, including microbes, plants and people, there are reactions that go more quickly or more slowly, depending on the temperature. Give three examples of situations in which people control temperature in order to control the growth or survival of living things. Include one or two examples of temperature control to encourage growth or survival, and one or two examples of temperature control to discourage growth or survival.

6 **a** What are enzymes? Find out one example of a plant enzyme and say what it does?

b The rates of reactions that involve enzymes depend on temperature. For any one example of an enzyme, find out and explain how this temperature-dependence affects the life cycle of the living thing.

c Digestion of starch is a chemical reaction that involves enzymes, alpha amylase and beta amylase. These are the results of an investigation on the total mass of starch that is digested over a period of three hours, with different enzymes present:

Time/hours	0.5	1.0	1.5	2.0	2.5	3.0
Starch digested with α amylase only/g	0.03	0.07	0.12	0.17	0.22	0.27
Starch digested with β amylase only/g	0.04	0.20	0.64	1.10	1.52	1.88
Starch digested with both enzymes /g	0.08	0.36	1.03	1.67	2.25	2.79

Plot these results onto a single pair of axes. Write a conclusion to say what these graphs tell you.

7 In hospital, it is often convenient to make up antibiotics for injections some time before use. What factors influence the shelf life of an antibiotic solution? Explain each of these factors.

8 Why are some antibiotics supplied as powder and made up into a syrup by a pharmacist for each individual prescription?

9 You have been asked to give a talk to your group on ways of monitoring rates of chemical reactions. You have an overhead projector (OHP) and permission to use the services of a laboratory technician. Make a list of the apparatus and chemicals you would need, and prepare sketches of the OHP transparencies you would want to present.

Monitoring and controlling devices

Defining the purpose of devices

Identifying the factors which affect the performance of devices

Varying key factors so that performance simply and efficiently matches purpose

LASER RADIATION

Hazards and safety

Targets

After working through this element you should:

- have prepared a report or reports on the factors which affect performance of a mechanical and an optical device, to show your achievement of the targets
- have reported in detail on how you set up a device and controlled one or more factors and monitored the effect on its performance
- have assessed performance of a mechanical device by direct observation and description, by making measurements, and by calculating efficiency
- have assessed performance of an optical device by direct observation and description and use of instruments such as light meters
- know that machines have input forces and output forces, usually called effort and load, and that machines are usually designed so that these forces are very different in size and/or direction
- know that input and output distances, speeds and sensitivities of machines are also usually very different
- know that in an ideal machine input power and useful output power would be the same, but in practice the useful output power is always smaller
- know that efficiency is a measure of this loss of power
- know that images are the outputs of optical devices, and that images can vary in their position, size and sharpness
- be able to use a variety of components to build simple devices and to vary the kinds of components and how they go together to achieve different required outputs

Cross references

The following pages in this book will also help you to achieve these targets:

50 Material properties

98 Light work

154 Choosing and using the right instrument

170 SI units and some definitions

172 Properties of substances

Key words

Some of the key words for this element are listed in the targets. These are some more:
force multiplier, distance multiplier, moment, pivot, newton (N), energy, joule (J), power, watt (W), normal, optical axis, object, real image, virtual image, converging, diverging, magnification, principal focus, focal length.

Case study: **Tension that heals**

▶ *Staff nurse Julie Lynch controls the tension in the string by controlling the amount of water in the bag*

▲ *Keeping the patient occupied is part of the job*

Accidents will happen, they say. Kyle Hayes is only two and a half, but he's learnt just how true it is. He fell out of his upstairs bedroom window. It could have been worse – his only injury was a broken thigh bone, and children's bones mend quickly. At Nottingham's Queen's Medical Centre they use string, plaster, gentle tensile forces and gentle care to make sure that the mend is a good one.

One way to try to hold bones still while they heal is to use plaster, of course. But plaster doesn't hold the muscles under tension, so they can still contract and move the bones out of position. And the plaster would have to be huge for a break like Kyle's – big enough to encase his hips and knee to ensure that the bones stay still. Another way is to operate and to fit screws and plates directly to the bone. For children, though, an operation isn't often needed. Traction, keeping the bone and surrounding muscle under tension, is less trouble to all concerned, especially the patient.

Kyle's foot has some freedom of movement inside a stirrup. One end of the stirrup is firmly attached to a pulley, and the other end to Kyle's leg by a tight bandage. Several metres of string are wrapped around a system of four pulleys, which uses the weight of a water bag and the weight of Kyle himself on the tilted bed to create the tension. When Kyle moves his leg the string runs through the pulleys and the water bag moves up or down, but the tension keeps pulling.

Every break is different, and children come in all shapes and sizes. So people like staff nurse Julie Lynch who set up the traction systems need to use subtle judgement to get it right every time. The age and size of the child, the type of fracture, whether the broken bones can move or not, and whether the skin is broken – these are some of the variables she has to take into account. Then she can set the position of the pulleys, the position of the knee sling, the tilt of the bed, and the weight of water in the bag.

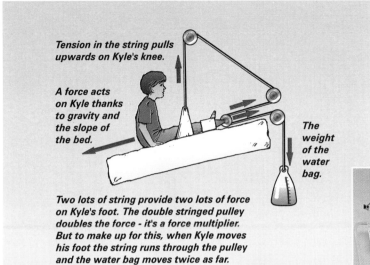

Tension in the string pulls upwards on Kyle's knee.

A force acts on Kyle thanks to gravity and the slope of the bed.

The weight of the water bag.

Two lots of string provide two lots of force on Kyle's foot. The double stringed pulley doubles the force - it's a force multiplier. But to make up for this, when Kyle moves his foot the string runs through the pulley and the water bag moves twice as far.

Children quickly get used to their limited movement. Their familiar books and toys, the TV, and even visits from celebrities help to keep boredom away. Just a few weeks after these pictures were taken Kyle was running around again as if nothing had ever happened. Except that he wasn't climbing onto his bedroom window sill.

Sister Hilary Holmes explains:

'Children can be on traction for 3 to 4 weeks but they settle very well. In traction you're keeping the muscle under tension and that helps to keep the bones in the correct position. It also cuts down muscle spasms which could pull the bones out of place.

With traction like Kyle's you get a three-way pull. You've got the slope of the bed so there's a force pulling him in the opposite direction to the string. You've also got the gentle upward pull of the knee sling. And since you've got two strings pulling on the foot pulley the force on the leg is twice the weight of the water bag.'

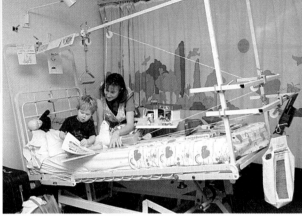

▼ Kyle's own weight at one end of the system and the water bag at the other create the tension in the string

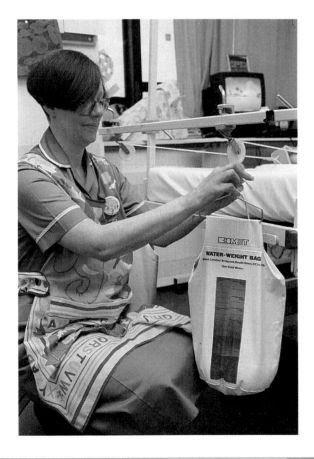

A ramp – a simple way to reduce the effort

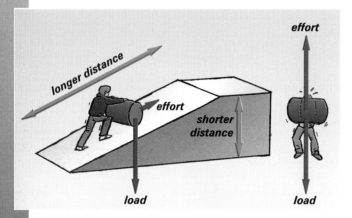

But to make up for the benefit you have to push for a longer distance.

Working and not working

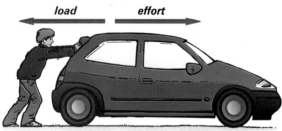

Working – force and distance

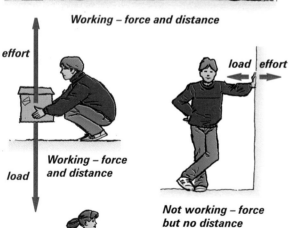

Working – force and distance

Not working – force but no distance

Not working – distance but no force

You can work out the amount of work done by multiplying force (in newtons) by distance (in metres). The answer will be in joules.

A hydraulic jack – double multiplication of your effort

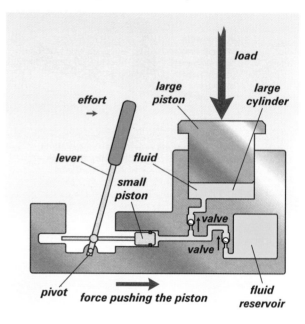

Multiplication one The handle acts as a lever. The effort acts a long way from the pivot to increase its turning effect or 'moment'.

Multiplication two Each movement of the small piston pumps a small amount of liquid into the large cylinder. The large piston only moves a small distance, but it can lift a large load.

Changing the direction...

The benefit of this is that it allows you to use your weight to pull down. Load and effort are about the same – it's the direction that's very different.

...and changing the size of the force

A pulley system – you have to pull the rope a long way compared with the distance you lift the load, but your effort is multiplied.

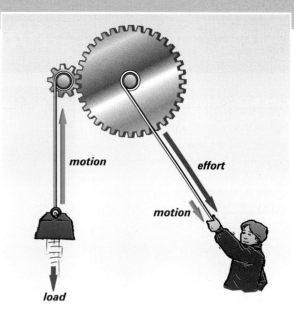

Put the system into reverse and you can multiply distance instead of force. You need a lot of effort but the speed of the load is much higher than the speed at which you pull the rope.

Teeth, cogs and gears

If you drive the small cog it makes a whole turn while the large cog only goes through a quarter of a turn. But the large cog exerts a force that's four times bigger than your driving force. The gear ratio is 4. Note that the number of teeth on the driven wheel is four times bigger than the number of teeth on the driving wheel.

A bicycle – a lot of speed for your effort

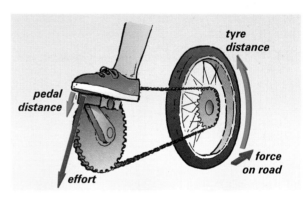

The force you exert on the pedal is bigger than the force of the tyre on the road, but you have the benefit of the extra distance and extra speed.

Magnifying distances

A small movement of one end of the lever results in a larger movement of the other end. Long needles on analogue clocks and meters increase their sensitivity.

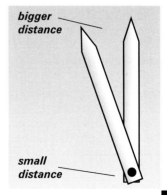

Shining

Light spreads out from a point and some enters your pupil. Your eye bends the cone of light back to a single point on your retina at the back of your eyeball.

Shining off

When a cone of light hits a plane mirror it keeps on spreading out.

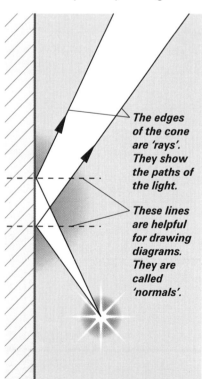

The edges of the cone are 'rays'. They show the paths of the light.

These lines are helpful for drawing diagrams. They are called 'normals'.

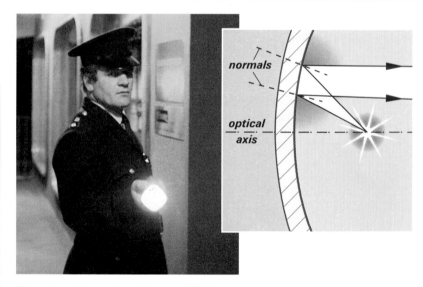

If you bend the mirror then you'll also change the shape of the beam of light. A concave mirror can stop light spreading out if the source of light is in the right place. It provides a narrow beam.

Shining through

A converging lens can focus a cone of light back to a single point. A microscope is a system of converging lenses.

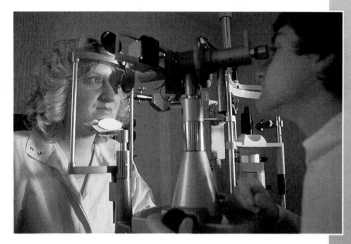

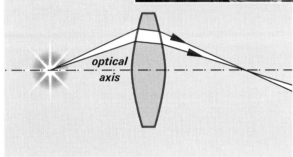

optical
axis

A diverging lens makes a wider cone of light. If you're short-sighted a diverging lens puts the problem right by making objects seem closer than they are.

A converging lens can provide a magnified image when the object is close to it.

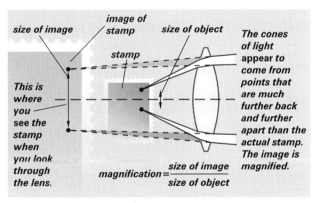

size of image

image of stamp

size of object

stamp

This is where you see the stamp when you look through the lens.

The cones of light appear to come from points that are much further back and further apart than the actual stamp. The image is magnified.

$$\text{magnification} = \frac{\text{size of image}}{\text{size of object}}$$

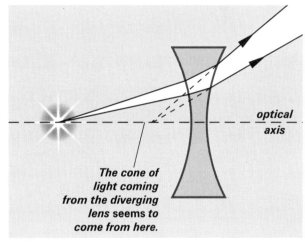

optical
axis

The cone of light coming from the diverging lens seems to come from here.

Shining through and off

In a 'through-the-lens' camera, the photographer sees the view through the lens and not through a completely separate viewfinder. Light reflects inside a prism on its way to the photographer's eye.

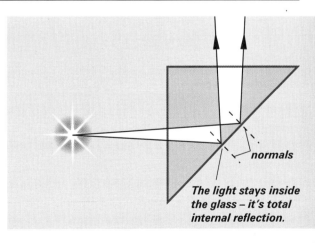

normals

The light stays inside the glass – it's total internal reflection.

Inputs and outputs...

...of machines

This table is about the inputs and outputs of a machine – this simple pulley system.

effort

load

	INPUTS	OUTPUTS
Forces (measured in newtons)	Effort	Force lifting the load (equal to the load itself)
Some force is needed to overcome the frictional forces acting on the moving pulley. So the effort will have to be bigger than the load.		
Work done or energy transferred (measured in joules)	Effort × distance moved (energy input)	Load × distance moved (useful work, or useful energy output)
The person pulling the rope is doing work – the work or energy input. Because of friction, not all of the energy input is transferred to the load. Some energy is transferred to the pulley and rope, and their temperature rises.		
Power (measured in watts)	Effort × speed (power input)	Load × speed (useful power output)
The speed at which the rope is pulled and the speed at which the load moves are the same in this case. But the effort is bigger than the load. So the power input is bigger than the useful power output.		

Power input – the rate at which energy is transferred from the chemical reaction of coal and oxygen.

Power output – the rate at which energy is transferred into the national electrical distribution system.

The turbine in a power station is a machine. The effort is provided by hot high-pressure steam. The load comes from magnetic forces between the moving coils that are carrying electric current.

There are many stages in a power station where the useful power output is less than the power input.

Power stations have an efficiency of about 40%.

Efficiency – a way of comparing useful power output with the power input.

$$\text{efficiency} = \frac{\text{useful power output}}{\text{power input}} \times 100\%$$

...of lenses

Converging lenses and focal length

A lens has a principal focus on either side of it. These are special points, because they are the only points that relate to parallel beams of light in such a simple way. The distance from a principal focus to the centre of the lens is called the focal length of the lens.

Objects and their images are the inputs and outputs of optical devices. The principal foci and the focal length give us a useful way to predict the kind of image we'll get from a particular object. It's a matter of knowing the rules that light and lenses obey.

Converging lenses with short focal lengths are fat and cause a beam of light to bend a lot. Converging lenses with long focal lengths bulge less and do less bending.

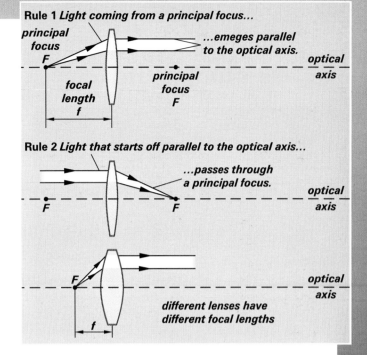

Rule 1 *Light coming from a principal focus...*

principal focus *F* ...*emeges parallel to the optical axis.*

optical axis

focal length f

principal focus F

Rule 2 *Light that starts off parallel to the optical axis...*

...*passes through a principal focus.*

optical axis

F *F*

F

optical axis

different lenses have different focal lengths

f

Describing images

When the object is close to the lens...
The image is:

▶ on the same side of the lens as the object
▶ further from the lens than the object
▶ magnified
▶ virtual – the name for an image that you cannot shine on to a screen
▶ the right way up.

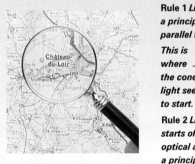

Rule 1 *Light coming from a principal focus emerges parallel to the optical axis.*

This is where the cone of light seems to start.

image
object
F *F*

Rule 2 *Light that starts off parallel to the optical axis passes through a principal focus.*

When the object is further from the lens...
The image is:

▶ on the opposite side of the lens to the object
▶ further from the lens than the object is
▶ magnified
▶ real – you can shine this image on to a screen
▶ upside down.

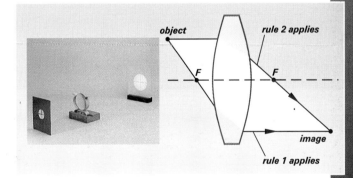

object   *rule 2 applies*

F   *F*

image

rule 1 applies

For diverging lenses the rules are slightly different...
The image is:

▶ on the same side of the lens as the object
▶ closer to the lens than the object is
▶ diminished (smaller than the object)
▶ virtual
▶ the right way up.

For a diverging lens, light that starts off parallel to the optical axis emerges from the direction of a principal focus.

This is where the cone of light seems to start.

object

F *F*

image

Light that starts off towards a principal focus emerges parallel to the optical axis.

Case study: **Photostudents**

▲ *Patsie Stafford-Johnson*

Patsie Stafford-Johnson, Carl Wheatley and Chris O'Reilly are three students learning how to be experts in photography, film and video of the living world. They're all students on the Biologiocal Imaging course at the University of Derby. Each of them has a different reason for starting the course, but they all have clear pictures of what they want to do. All the photos on these four pages were taken by these students.

Bright lights and wild life. That's what Patsie Stafford-Johnson goes looking for when she goes on holiday. The bright lights could be the intense sun in the Namib deserts and the wildlife might be the dense greenery of South American jungles.

Patsie used to be a nurse. She would save her money so that she could travel with her camera to places that are hardly touched by humans. Now she's improving her skills and know-how so that she can share her vision of the natural world with many more people.

The camera has the capability to produce sharp images from close up or from a distance. Patsie has the capability to control the camera to get the results she wants.

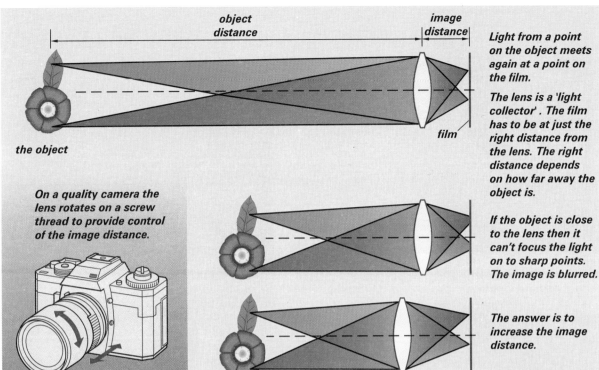

On a quality camera the lens rotates on a screw thread to provide control of the image distance.

Light from a point on the object meets again at a point on the film.

The lens is a 'light collector'. The film has to be at just the right distance from the lens. The right distance depends on how far away the object is.

If the object is close to the lens then it can't focus the light on to sharp points. The image is blurred.

The answer is to increase the image distance.

▲ *How to get sharp images from near and from far objects.*

Sharp images are good, blurred images are bad? Not always. Patsie has deliberately taken a picture with a narrow depth of field. The blurred background makes the flowers stand out.

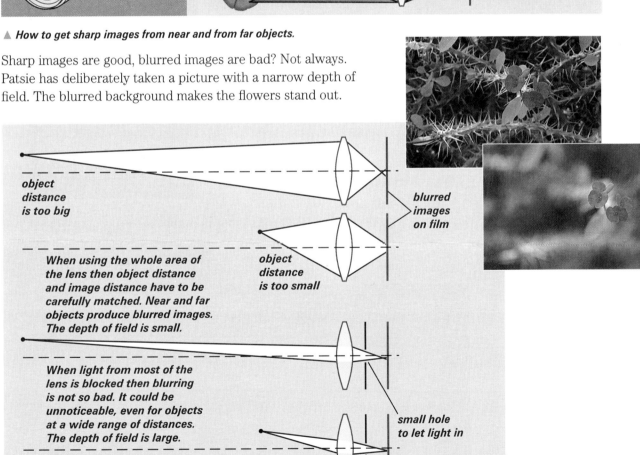

When using the whole area of the lens then object distance and image distance have to be carefully matched. Near and far objects produce blurred images. The depth of field is small.

When light from most of the lens is blocked then blurring is not so bad. It could be unnoticeable, even for objects at a wide range of distances. The depth of field is large.

▲ *Controlling depth of field.*

▲ Light from behind shows up the intricate shapes of fungus.

These pictures by Patsie show that it's not just the film and the camera that can be used to achieve different effects. The light on the subject is the most important factor of all.

▶ Bright light from the top and front makes the most of the colour of these flowers. A touch of shadow adds to the sharp feel of the picture.

▶ If there's no natural light, create your own. Artificial light makes the subject bright, while the background is black.

◀ Subdued light from the side creates shadows that help to show up the main veins on a leaf. An eye for every detail is one of the skills of a good photographer.

Carl Wheatley has an eye on a career as a police photographer or in forensic science. His work then will involve analysing photographic evidence or taking scene of the crime photographs. He knows how to use lenses to get a close-up shot without having to get close up to the subject. The key factor here is the focal length of the lens.

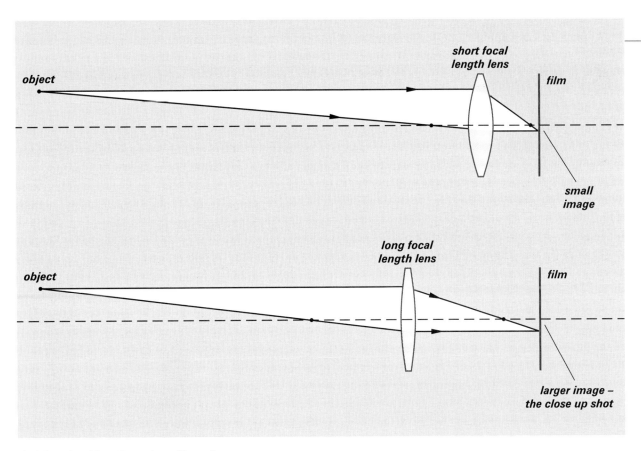

▲ *A long focal length creates a bigger image*

Same fern leaves, different pictures. Chris O'Reilly has used a tripod to keep his camera steady, then he's kept the shutter open for a longer time to get the brighter picture. In photography, exposure time is crucial in controlling the outcome.

Chris worked in design before he went back to being a student. Now he's hoping to move into a branch of biological research in which his special imaging skills will be useful.

1 Read about Hugh Barton's emergency railway lamp in 'Light work' in chapter 3.3.

   a Draw a diagram of the light bulb, the curved reflector and the lens.

   b The reflector creates a fairly narrow beam of light – instead of spreading out it retains its intensity over long distances. Why did Hugh choose to use the reflector to do this, rather than using a specially shaped lens? What shape would such a lens have to be? What focal length would it have, compared to the dimensions of the lamp?

2 Read 'Tension that heals'. Use pulleys and other materials to build a model of Kyle's traction system.

   a Investigate how varying the weight of water in the bag affects the tension in the 'leg' in your model.

   b Why have two strings attached to the foot, rather than just one?

   c What would happen if the slope of the bed changes?

   d Use your model to investigate how the arrangement might need to change for an older patient, say a ten year old child.

3 A broken bone can be repaired using screws and plates.

   a Why would this be unsuitable for a young child like Kyle?

   b What would be the important properties of materials used in such plates and screws?

4 Read 'Photostudents'. Professional photographers often 'bracket' their shots. They take several shots of the same subject to make sure that they get a good exposure in at least one of them.

   Use an SLR camera to take several shots of the same subject. Vary the camera setting each time and record the setting for each shot. Make a display of your shots, and use the information in 'Photostudents' to help you to explain the different appearance of each one.

5 Compare a simple fixed lens snapshot camera with an expensive SLR camera. Explain the advantages of the SLR camera, and how it achieves these advantages. Use the information in 'Photostudents' to help you with your explanations. Include diagrams.

6 Obtain two telescopes or two pairs of binoculars. Devise laboratory tests for comparing the quality of images of the two instruments.

7 Investigate the images from a number of lenses of different focal lengths. Vary the distances of the object from each lens. Describe the position of the object as either:

   object is less than the focal length away from the lens

   object is between one and two focal lengths away from the lens

   object is more than two focal lengths from the lens.

   Describe the images in each case. Try to identify rules that relate type of image to object position.

8 A lever is a simple machine.

   a Is it always a force multiplier, always a distance multiplier, or can it be both?

   b Set up a simple lever and make measurements on the effort, the load, and their distances from the pivot. Do this for various values of the forces and distances, and record the results.

   c Can you discover a mathematical rule that relates these four quantities together?

9 A garage mechanic uses a hydraulic jack to lift a car, pulling the handle a distance of 0.5 m once every second. The force needed is 160 N.

   a Use work = force × distance to calculate the work done by the mechanic,
   (i) on each pull of the handle
   (ii) after 20 pulls of the handle.

   b Use power = work /time to calculate the effective power of the mechanic while doing this work.

   c What would be the power if the mechanic pulled the handle twice every second, i.e. if the time for each pull were 0.5 s.

   d The jack lifts a load of 7500 N through a distance of 0.2 m in 25 s. What is the total work done on the load?

   e What is the power output of the jack?

   f The answer to part b) is the power input to the jack. What is its efficiency?

Reference section

Measuring volumes of liquids using measuring cylinders

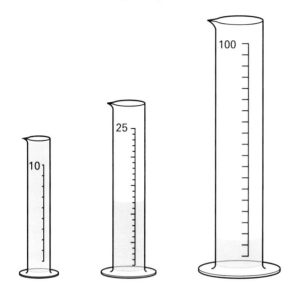

The smallest cylinder is not large enough to measure all the liquid.

The largest cylinder can only measure to the nearest 5 cm^3.

The 25 cm^3 cylinder is the most suitable. It can measure all the liquid, and it has finer divisions than the largest one.

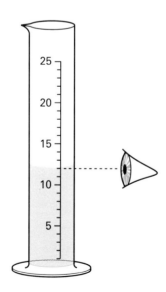

The position of the bottom of the meniscus provides the reading. This reading is 12 cm^3.

Measuring the thickness of a wire

There are two devices which can measure thicknesses to a much more precise level than a rule.

Micrometer screw gauge

The micrometer measures distances of a few millimetres, to the nearest 0.01 mm.

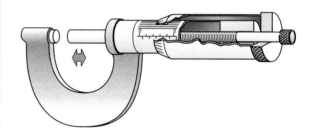

The micrometer acts as a machine that multiplies a small distance into a big one. The result is that a micrometer is a sensitive instrument.

Vernier callipers

Vernier callipers measure to the nearest 0.1 mm and can be used to measure thicknesses up to several centimetres.

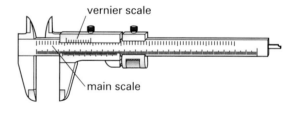

The position of the vernier zero against the main scale gives the approximate distance between the jaws. The next level of precision is given by the mark on the vernier scale that exactly coincides with a mark on the main scale.

Electrical measurements

Measuring electric current

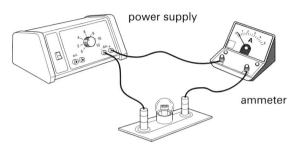

power supply

ammeter

An ammeter measures the current flowing in a circuit. The ammeter might be digital or analogue. The ammeter is connected in series in the circuit so that the current it measures flows through it.

Measuring potential difference

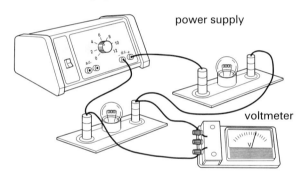

power supply

voltmeter

A voltmeter measures the voltage (the potential difference) between two points in a circuit. It's connected in parallel, not in series.

Trouble-shooting

▶ The needle moves off the end of the scale – the current or voltage is too high, switch off so that you do not damage the meter, and check the range of the meter.

▶ The needle moves in the wrong direction – switch off and then reverse the connections.

▶ A digital meter may show a negative value if the connections are the wrong way round – ignore the negative sign or reverse the connections.

▶ Some meters have two or more scales – make sure you are using the right scale for the range you are using.

How do you decide which is the right thermometer for the job?

Accurate?

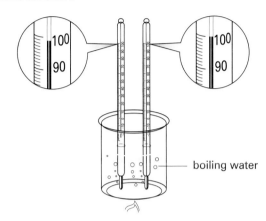

boiling water

These laboratory thermometers cost less than £1 each. One reads 99 °C and the other reads 100 °C. The second one is more accurate.

Sensitive?

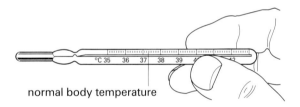

normal body temperature

When we measure body temperature small changes are important. This clinical thermometer can measure to the nearest 0.1 °C. But its range is narrow – it can only measure between 35 °C and 43 °C.

Wide range?

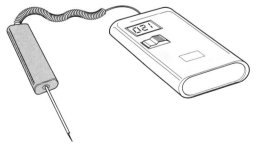

Electronic thermometers use 'thermocouple probes'. They can operate between −273 °C and +1200 °C.

Bar charts

A bar chart is a useful way to compare figures. This chart compares the thermal conductivities of different metals.

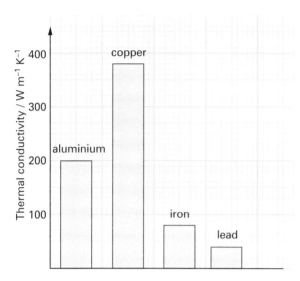

Graph paper is useful, but lined paper is a good substitute. The height of the bar gives the thermal conductivity for each metal. Shading or colouring makes the different bars stand out.

Calculating percentages and drawing pie charts

Computer spreadsheets provide an efficient way of converting raw data into a pie chart. These are the principles behind what the computer does for you.

The sectors of a pie chart show how something is divided up, often in percentages. The land of a market garden is divided between different crops, like this:

area growing potatoes   = 0.4 hectares (ha)
area growing leeks   = 0.6 hectares
area growing cabbages   = 1.0 hectares
total area of market garden = 2.0 hectares

To draw the pie chart, it helps to start with a circle divided into 10 sectors. Divide the circle in half vertically then use a protractor. Each 10 sector needs 36 degrees.

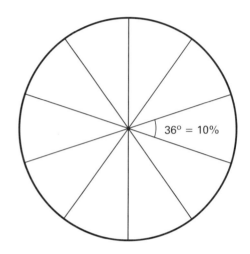

Now work out the percentage for each crop:

$$\text{area growing potatoes} = \frac{0.4}{2.0} \times 100\% = 20\%$$

You can do this quickly in a table:

CROP	AREA /ha	PERCENTAGE	SECTORS
Potatoes	0.4	$\frac{0.4}{2.0} \times 100\% = 20\%$	2
Leeks	0.6	$\frac{0.6}{2.0} \times 100\% = 30\%$	3
Cabbages	1.0	$\frac{1.0}{2.0} \times 100\% = 50\%$	5

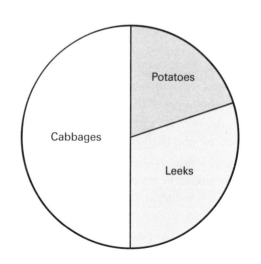

Finding patterns

These results are for an investigation of a pulley system:

LOAD /N	EFFORT /N
5	18
4	16
8	25
10	30
2	13
12	36
6	20

arrange in order
to see the pattern →

LOAD /N	EFFORT /N
2	13
4	16
5	18
6	20
8	25
10	30
12	36

A graph can show any pattern more clearly.

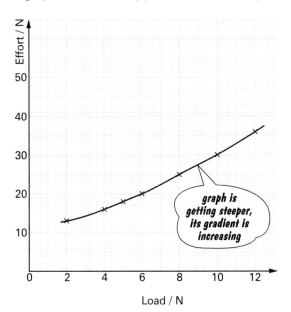

graph is getting steeper, its gradient is increasing

Simple tables and simple graphs

Two students have designed and made an electrical heater for a plant propagator. They tested it in a container of damp soil.

They record their results in a table:

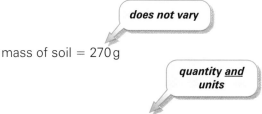

does not vary

mass of soil = 270 g

quantity _and_ units

TIME/min	TEMPERATURE/°C
0	19
1	20
2	23
3	24
4	26
5	29
6	34
7	33

suspect result

They also recorded their results as a graph:

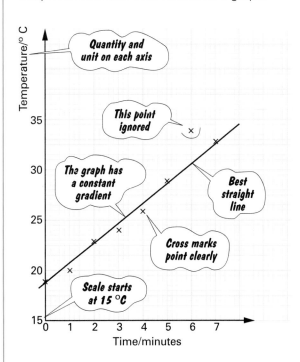

Quantity and unit on each axis

This point ignored

The graph has a constant gradient

Best straight line

Cross marks point clearly

Scale starts at 15 °C

Visual information

Graphs are a clear way of showing information. Just by looking at the shape of a graph we can get a basic idea of what's happening. More careful inspection can give us detailed information.

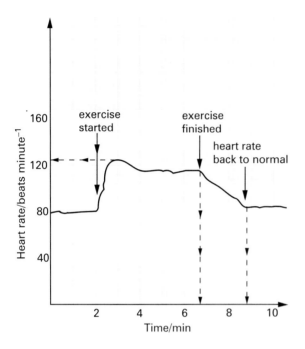

This graph shows that an athlete's heart rate increased during training. We can also read from the graph to find out the athlete's greatest heart rate and the time it took for the heart rate to go back to normal after the exercise stopped.

Calibration curves

Graphs can be used to provide detailed specific information based on general relationships.

In this example, a range of vitamin C solutions are used to remove the colour from a blue indicator, called DCPIP. As the concentration of the vitamin C solution is increased, a smaller volume of the solution is needed to remove the colour from the indicator.

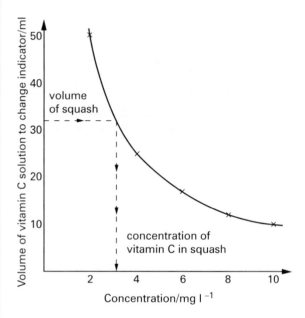

This calibration graph can be used to find the vitamin C concentration of any solution. For example, it can tell us the vitamin C concentration in some orange squash.

When orange squash is added to the indicator, it takes $32\,cm^3$ of squash to remove the DCPIP colour. From the graph you can work out the concentration of vitamin C in the squash.

Graph gradients

These are typical measurements of resistance of different lengths of a wire.

LENGTH/m	RESISTANCE/Ω
0.21	1.5
0.40	2.9
0.58	4.8
0.82	5.5
1.01	7.1

A graph displays the relationship between length and resistance. Notice from the graph that doubling the length of the wire always doubles its resistance. In fact, whatever changes happen to the length, the resistance always changes by the same proportion. The resistance is proportional to the length.

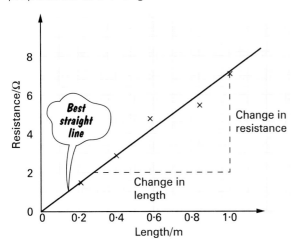

Measuring the gradient of the graph gives us more information that's useful.

$$\text{gradient} = \frac{\text{change in resistance}}{\text{change in length}}$$

$$= \frac{7.2\,\Omega - 2.0\,\Omega}{1.0\,\text{m} - 0.28\,\text{m}}$$

(you show units with numbers at first)

$$= \frac{5.2}{0.72}$$

(you leave out units during calculation)

$$= 7.2\,\Omega\text{m}^{-1}$$

(you *must* show the unit with the answer)

$7.2\,\Omega$ is the resistance of 1 m of the wire. So now it's easier to work out the resistance of any length of wire. 10 cm of wire will have a resistance of $0.72\,\Omega$, and so on.

Straight line graphs

A graph is a display of the relationship between variables. In an experiment to find out about a relationship it is conventional to show the variables as follows:

▶ on the x-axis – independent variable – the variable that you change

▶ on the y-axis – dependent variable – the variable which changes as a result.

The line on a graph can have many kinds of shapes, but straight lines are the simplest.

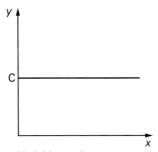

Variable x: changes
Variable y: doesn't change
Relationship: y does not depend upon x but is constant
Mathematical relationship: y = C (C stands for constant)

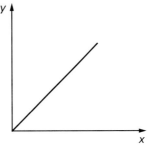

Variable x: changes
Variable y: always changes by the same *proportion* as x
Relationship: y is proportional to x
Mathematical relationship: y = kx
Note that the gradient of the line is constant. k is the gradient

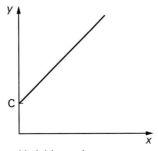

Variable x: changes
Variable y: increases as x increases but is not proportional
Mathematical relationship: y = kx + C
k is still the constant gradient of the graph
Note that when x is zero y equals C
C is the intercept of the graph

The basic units that we use are human sized. A metre is about the height of an adult from the ground to the waist, a kilogram is the mass of a large book, and a second is about the time it takes to say your name.

A lot of scientific work deals with numbers that are very small or very big. It is convenient to have a quick way of writing big and small numbers. Powers of ten do this job.

Positive powers

$10^1 = 10$
$10^2 = 10 \times 10 = 100$
$10^3 = 10 \times 10 \times 10 = 1000$
and so on.
Note that
$10^2 + 10^2 = 2 \times 10^2 = 200$
but that
$10^3 \times 10^3 = 10^6 = 1\,000\,000$
Note also that
$10^0 = 1$

Negative powers

$10^{-1} = 1 \div 10 = 0.1$
$10^{-2} = 1 \div (10 \times 10) = 0.01$
$10^{-3} = 1 \div (10 \times 10 \times 10) = 0.001$
and so on.
Note that
$10^{-1} + 10^{-1} = 2 \times 10^{-1} = 0.2$
but that
$10^{-2} \times 10^{-3} = 10^{-5} = 0.00001$

The scale below gives some examples of lengths, masses and times.

10^{-10}	10^{-9}	10^{-8}	10^{-7}	10^{-6}	10^{-5}	10^{-4}	10^{-3}	10^{-2}	10^{-1}	10^0	10^1	10^2	10^3	10^4	10^5	10^6	10^7	10^8	10^9	10^{10}	10^{11}	10

Some lengths

10^{-10} m
diameter of hydrogen atom

2×10^{-6} m
diameter of staphylo-coccus bacterium

10^{-4} m
thickness of paper

10^{-1} m
width of adult hand

10^2 m
distance an athlete can sprint in 10 seconds

10^4 m
maximum depth of oceans

1.2×10^7 m
diameter of Earth

1.5×10^{11}
distance from Earth to Sun

Some masses

10^{-7} kg
grain of sand

1.5×10^{-2} kg
house mouse

4 kg
house brick

6.5×10^2 kg
small car

10^5 kg
blue whale

3×10^8 kg
laden supertanker

Some times

10^{-8} s
time for light to cross a room

10^{-1} s
human reaction time

10 s
time for athlete to sprint 100 m

5×10^2 s
time for light to travel from Sun to Earth

10^5 s
1 day

2×10^9 s
human life span

Using a microscope

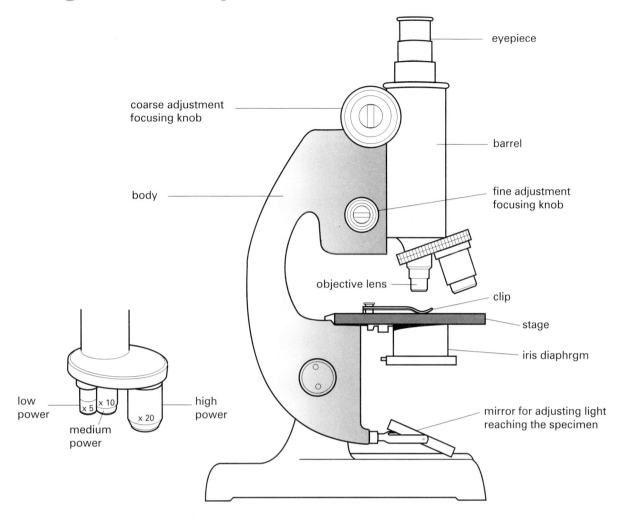

A compound microscope. Note that the barrel moves up and down for focusing

Microscopes extend our view of the world. They enable us to distinguish small objects which our eyes alone cannot resolve. A high resolution microscope is able to distinguish objects that are very close together. The best optical microscopes can help the human eye to distinguish between objects that are less than 10^{-6} m apart.

Important points to note when setting up your microscope:

▶ Initially use the smallest (low power) objective lens to view the specimen.

▶ Direct light onto the mirror to illuminate the specimen. Do NOT focus sunlight through the microscope onto your eye.

▶ Adjust the iris diaphragm below the stage to control the amount of light. (You may not need very bright light to obtain the best image.)

▶ Start with the objective lens close to the specimen, checking that the objective does not touch the specimen. Gradually raise the objective lens until the image is in focus.

▶ When the specimen is clearly in focus with the low power lens, change to a higher power objective to improve the resolution. Take care that the higher power objective does not touch the specimen as you rotate it into position.

Calculating density

When we are doing calculations about density we use the formula:

$$\text{density} = \frac{\text{mass}}{\text{volume}}$$

We can write the same formula more quickly if we just write:

$$\rho = \frac{m}{V}$$

ρ is a standard abbreviation for density.

An example

In an experiment to find the density of a block of wood, the block weighed 3 kg and had a volume of 0.004 m^3.

We can write these results down like this:

$$m = 3\,\text{kg} \qquad V = 0.004\,\text{m}^3$$

We can then replace the letters in the formula:

$$\rho = \frac{m}{V}$$

with the numbers:

$$\rho = \frac{3\,\text{kg}}{0.004\,\text{m}^3}$$

r = 3 ÷ 0.004

Now we can use a calculator to find the value for the density:

$$\rho = 750\,\text{kg}\,\text{m}^{-3}$$

Another example

In an investigation of a pulley system, a 200 newton force works through a distance of 5 metres.

To find the work done (energy transfer) we use the formula:

$$\text{work done} = \text{force} \times \text{distance}$$

We would write that in symbols as:

$$W = F \times s$$

or even more simply:

$$W = Fs$$

To find the work done we write $F = 200\,\text{N}$ and $s = 5\,\text{m}$.

$$W = F \times s$$
$$W = 200\,\text{N} \times 5\,\text{m}$$
$$W = 1000\,\text{J}$$

Rearrangements of formulas

On page 171 of the 'Reference section' you will find the formulas you may need to use. This table shows the various rearrangements of the formulas.

ρ = density
m = mass
V = volume

$$\rho = \frac{m}{V} \qquad m = \rho V \qquad V = \frac{m}{\rho}$$

v = speed
s = distance
t = time

$$v = \frac{s}{t} \qquad s = vt \qquad t = \frac{s}{v}$$

W = work done
F = force
s = distance

$$W = Fs \qquad F = \frac{W}{s} \qquad s = \frac{W}{F}$$

P = power
W = work done
t = time

$$P = \frac{W}{t} \qquad t = \frac{W}{P} \qquad W = Pt$$

R = resistance
V = potential difference
I = current

$$R = \frac{V}{I} \qquad V = IR \qquad I = \frac{V}{R}$$

P = power
V = potential difference
I = current

$$P = VI \qquad V = \frac{P}{I} \qquad I = \frac{P}{V}$$

Rearranging your own formulas

To rearrange a formula there is a simple rule: you can change any equation as much as you like – as long as you always do the same thing to both sides.

For example, $R = \frac{V}{I}$ is very helpful if you want to find R, but what if you need to find I?

You need to rearrange the formula so that I is left alone on the left-hand side of the formula.

$$R = \frac{V}{I}$$

Multiply both sides by I:

$$I \times R = \frac{V}{I} \times I$$

change both sides in the same way

Which is the same as:

$$IR = V$$

Divide both sides by R:

$$\frac{IR}{R} = \frac{V}{R}$$

change both sides in the same way

Which gives us:

$$I = \frac{V}{R}$$

Note that during this process we have also shown how to work out V:

$$V = IR$$

Chemical formulas in equations

To provide precise information about a substance, chemists have developed a system of symbols and formulas to describe substances.

Each element has a symbol of one or two letters. (See the table on page 176 of the 'Reference section' for a list of symbols.)

Compounds are described by a formula which shows the elements that make up the compound.

Writing formulas

Type of substance	Examples
Elements with a giant structure of atoms – write the symbol for the atom	■ All metals (e.g. Mg, Fe, Ca, Na) ■ Some non-metals (e.g. C, Si)
Elements which are molecular – write the formula of the molecule	■ Many non-metals (e.g. Cl_2, O_2, H_2)
Compounds which are molecular – write the formula of the molecule	■ Most compounds of non-metals with non-metals (e.g. H_2O, CO_2, HCl, CH_3OH)
Compounds with giant structures – write the simplest formula of the compound	■ Salts with giant structures of ions (e.g. NaCl, $CaCl_2$, Na_2SO_4, $Mg(NO_3)_2$)

An example of a molecular compound:

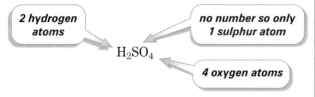

2 hydrogen atoms

no number so only 1 sulphur atom

H_2SO_4

4 oxygen atoms

An example of a giant structure compound:

there is 1 magnesium ion

$Mg(NO_3)_2$

for every 2 nitrate ions

Formulas of ionic compounds

Every ionic compound contains positive ions combined with negative ions. The total positive charge in the formula must equal the total negative charge.

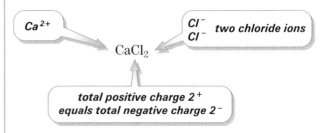

Ca^{2+}

Cl^-
 Cl^- two chloride ions

$CaCl_2$

total positive charge 2^+ equals total negative charge 2^-

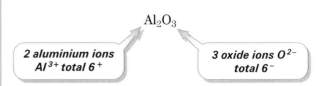

Al_2O_3

2 aluminium ions Al^{3+} total 6^+

3 oxide ions O^{2-} total 6^-

Chemical equations

Examples of word equations

In a 'word equation' write the names of the reactants on the left and the products on the right.

Neutralization

$$acid + base \longrightarrow salt + water$$

Example

$$sulphuric\ acid + sodium\ hydroxide \longrightarrow$$
$$sodium\ sulphate + water$$

Redox

Example

$$iron\ oxide + carbon \longrightarrow$$
$$iron + carbon\ dioxide$$

Esterification

$$alcohol + alkanoic\ acid \longrightarrow ester + water$$

Example

$$ethanol + methanoic\ acid \longrightarrow$$
$$ethyl\ methanoate + water$$

Balanced symbol equations

Step 1 Write down the word equation.

Step 2 Underneath, write down the formula of each reactant and product.

Step 3 Check to see if the equation needs balancing – are there the same number of atoms of each element on each side of the equation?

Step 4 Balance the equation by writing numbers in front of formulas (do not change formulas).

Example

Step 1 sodium hydroxide + hydrochloric acid $\longrightarrow$ sodium chloride + water

Step 2

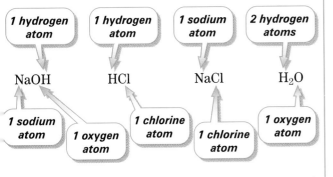

Step 3

1 sodium atom	1 sodium atom
1 oxygen atom	1 oxygen atom
(1 + 1) hydrogen atoms	2 hydrogen atoms
1 chlorine atom	1 chlorine atom

Step 4 $NaOH + HCl \longrightarrow NaCl + H_2O$

The equation balances.

Another example

Step 1 sulphuric acid + sodium hydroxide $\longrightarrow$ sodium sulphate + water

Step 2

$$H_2SO_4 \qquad NaOH \qquad Na_2SO_4 \qquad H_2O$$

Step 3

1 sulphur atom	1 sulphur atom
(4 + 1) oxygen atoms	(4 + 1) oxygen atoms
(2 + 1) hydrogen atoms	2 hydrogen atoms
1 sodium atom	2 sodium atoms

Step 4 The equation does not balance. Balance the equation by writing numbers in front of formulas (do not change formulas)

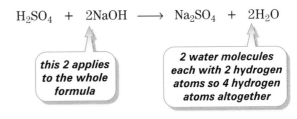

1 sulphur atom	1 sulphur atom
(4 + 2) oxygen atoms	(4 + 2) oxygen atoms
(2 + 2) hydrogen atoms	4 hydrogen atoms
2 sodium atoms	2 sodium atoms

Now the equation balances.

Quantities of chemicals

QUANTITY	COMMON UNITS	MEANING
Mass	gram (g) kilogram (kg) 1 kg = 1000 g	Samples with the same mass give the same reading on a balance
Volume	cubic centimetre, (cm^3) litre (l or dm^3) 1 litre = 1 dm^3 = 1000 cm^3	Samples with the same volume take up the same amount of space. Two liquids with the same volume for example, fill a measuring cylinder to the same level
Amount	mole (mol)	Samples with the same amount of a chemical contain the same number of atoms, molecules or ions. There are as many atoms in one mole of carbon as there are molecules in one mole of water

Relative atomic masses

A hydrogen atom is the lightest atom. On the relative atomic mass scale, the relative mass of hydrogen is 1.

All other atoms have more mass.

The relative atomic mass of carbon is 12; a carbon atom is 12 times heavier than a hydrogen atom.

An oxygen atom is 16 times heavier than a hydrogen atom, so oxygen's relative atomic mass is 16.

A_r is the symbol for relative atomic mass.

For example:

A_r (H) = 1,
A_r (C) = 12,
A_r (O) = 16,
A_r (Na) = 23,
A_r (Cl) = 35.5.

See the table on page 176 of the 'Reference section' for other values of relative atomic mass.

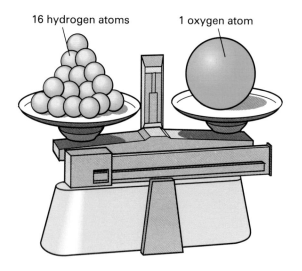

16 hydrogen atoms   1 oxygen atom

Relative formula masses

Count up the relative atomic masses in the formula of a substance to find the relative formula mass.

The formula for water is H_2O, so its total relative formula mass is 2×1 for the hydrogen and 16 for the oxygen. That is a total of 18.

So a water molecule is 18 times heavier than a hydrogen atom.

Amounts in moles

Elements

The mass of one mole (mol) of atoms of an element is its relative atomic mass in grams.

Examples

The mass of 1 mol hydrogen atoms = $1 \times 1 = 1\,g$
The mass of 1 mol carbon atoms = $12\,g$
The mass of 2 mol chlorine atoms = $2 \times 35.5 = 71\,g$
The mass of 3 mol of sodium atoms = $3 \times 23 = 69\,g$

Compounds

The mass of one mole of a compound is its relative formula mass in grams.

Examples:

The mass of 1 mol sodium hydroxide,
$NaOH = (23 + 16 + 1)\,g = 40\,g$

The mass of 1 mol carbon dioxide,
$CO_2 = [12 + (2 \times 16)]\,g = 44\,g$

Masses and amounts

The mass of a sample (g) =
  number of moles × mass of one mole (g)

The number of moles of a substance =
  mass of sample (g) ÷ mass of one mole (g)

Amounts in equations and how to calculate yield

The equation for a reaction shows the amounts of chemicals involved as reactants and products.

Example

$$H_2SO_4 \ + \ 2NaOH \longrightarrow \ Na_2SO_4 \ + \ 2H_2O$$

1 mol   2 mol   1 mol   2 mol

So the reacting masses are:

$$98\,g \ + \ (2 \times 40)\,g \ = \ 178\,g \longrightarrow$$
$$142\,g \ + \ (2 \times 18)\,g \ = \ 178\,g$$

Note that the total mass of products must equal the total mass of reactants if the equation balances.

Note also that a reaction which starts with 80 g of sodium hydroxide should produce 142 g of sodium sulphate. In practice, though the yield of sodium sulphate will be less than this.

Scale the amounts up or down to match the quantities in a laboratory or industrial preparation.

For example, if the experiment started with 8 g sodium hydroxide this would be one tenth of the mass of sodium hydroxide needed to produce a mole of sodium sulphate.

So the theoretical yield of sodium sulphate would be $\dfrac{142\,g}{10} = 14.2\,g$.

If the actual yield is only 12.0 g, then the percentage yield = $(12.0 \div 14.2) \times 100\% = 85\%$

In chemistry we measure concentrations in moles per dm^3. ($1\,dm^3$ is also called 1 litre.)

A solution that contains one mole of solute in $1\,dm^3$ of solution has a concentration of $1.0\,mol\,dm^{-3}$.

This is sometimes called a molar solution, or 1.0 M for short.

> concentration = amount of solute ÷ volume of solution

Titration

Titration is a way of measuring the concentration of a solution, by using another solution which has a concentration that you already know.

The commonest type of titration is with an alkali and an acid – a neutralization reaction.

The flask in the diagram contains a measured volume of alkali with a few drops of indicator. The indicator is a substance that changes colour when neutralization is complete. That is called the end point of the titration.

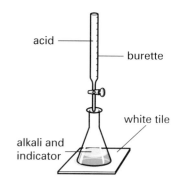

Acid is slowly added to the flask from the burette, drop by drop and it is swirled to mix the acid and alkali. The burette provides a measurement of the volume of acid that is needed to reach the end point.

Example

A technician needs to know the concentration of some sulphuric acid. She makes up a solution of sodium hydroxide with a concentration of $1.0\,mol\,dm^{-3}$. She puts $20\,cm^3$ of the solution into a clean flask, and puts the acid into the burette.

At the end point, $12.5\,cm^3$ of acid have run out of the burette.

The equation for this reaction is: sulphuric acid + sodium hydroxide $\longrightarrow$ sodium sulphate + water

$$H_2SO_4 \quad + \quad 2NaOH \quad \longrightarrow \quad Na_2SO_4 \quad + \quad 2H_2O$$

This tells us that it takes 2 mol of sodium hydroxide to neutralize 1 mol of sulphuric acid. So at the end point, there are twice as many mol of alkali as acid.

$$\frac{\text{amount of acid}}{\text{amount of alkali}} = \frac{1\,mol}{2\,mol}$$

Remember that: concentration = amount of solute ÷ volume of solution

So: $\dfrac{\text{concentration of acid}}{\text{concentration of alkali}} = \dfrac{\text{amount of acid} \div \text{volume of acid from burette}}{\text{amount of alkali} \div \text{volume of alkali in flask}}$

The values of most of these quantities are known. The numbers can go into the formula:

$$\frac{\text{concentration of acid}}{1.0\,mol\,dm^{-3}} = \frac{1\,mol \div 12.5\,cm^3}{2\,mol \div 20\,cm^3}$$

$$\frac{\text{concentration of acid}}{1.0} = \frac{0.08}{0.10}$$

$$\frac{\text{concentration of acid}}{1.0} = 0.8$$

$$\text{concentration of acid} = 0.8\,mol\,dm^{-3}$$

What is an average?

An average value for a set of figures can mean a 'typical' value. For example, we might say that the average height for men is 1.80 m. We mean that this is the typical height we might expect a man to be.

In different sets of data, we may use different ways of obtaining a value which is truly typical of the whole set of values.

Mode

The mode of a set of values is the one which occurs most often. For example, a shoe manufacturer might be most interested in knowing that the most common ladies' shoe size is 36.

Mean

The mean value is calculated:

$$\text{mean} = \frac{\text{sum of all the values}}{\text{number of values}}$$

The mean is very commonly used to find the 'average'.

Median

The median of a set of values is the middle value when all the values are put in order (or the mean of the middle pair if there is an even number of values). Half the values in the set will be greater than the median and half the values will be less than the median.

Often a judgement has to be made to decide which method of finding the 'average' gives a typical value for the whole set of data.

For example in a small company with 20 employees, the weekly wages of the employees are:

£200, £200, £200, £200, £200, £250, £250, £250, £300, £300, £300, £300, £350, £350, £350, £450, £450, £600, £1000, £1500

Since the values have been set in order it is easy to see that the median value is £300.

$$\text{mean} = \frac{\text{total wages}}{\text{number of employees}}$$

$$\text{mean} = \frac{£8000}{20}$$

$$\text{mean} = £400$$

A prospective employee who was told that the 'average' wage was £400 would probably be disappointed when s/he found out what s/he would earn, since 15 out of the 20 employees earn less than the mean wage. The median wage of £300 would be a much more representative figure. The mean is higher because of the very high wages of just two employees.

There are standard international units for all the quantities people measure in science.

Some basic SI units

QUANTITY	SYMBOL	UNIT	UNIT SYMBOL
Length	l	metre	m
Mass	m	kilogram	kg
Time	t	second	s
Electric current	I	ampere	A
Temperature	T	kelvin	K
Amount of substance		mole	mol

Some more SI units

QUANTITY	SYMBOL	UNIT	UNIT SYMBOL
Area	A	square metre	m^2
Volume	V	cubic metre *	m^3
Speed	v	metre per second	$m\,s^{-1}$
Density	ρ	kilogram per cubic metre	$kg\,m^{-3}$
Force	F	newton	N
Pressure and stress	p	pascal	Pa
Work and energy	W	joule	J
Power	P	watt	W
Electric potential difference (voltage)	V	volt	V
Electric resistance	R	ohm	Ω
Electrical resistivity	ρ	ohm metre	$\Omega\,m$

* You will also see volume measured in decimetre cubed (dm^3) and litre (l). $1\,dm^3 = 1\,l = 10^{-3}\,m^3$

Some SI prefixes for large and small numbers

NUMBER	SUB-MULTIPLE	PREFIX	SYMBOL
1/100 or	10^{-2}	centi	c
1/1000 or	10^{-3}	milli	m
1/1 000 000 or	10^{-6}	micro	μ
1/1 000 000 000 or	10^{-9}	nano	n

For example, a millimetre is one thousandth of a metre, or 10^{-3} m.

NUMBER	SUB-MULTIPLE	PREFIX	SYMBOL
1000 or	10^{3}	kilo	k
1 000 000 or	10^{6}	mega	M
1 000 000 000 or	10^{9}	giga	G

A kilogram is a thousand grams. However, a million grams is not called a megagram but a tonne

Some quantities with units and definitions

WORD EQUATION	SYMBOL	UNIT	DEFINITION
speed $= \dfrac{\text{distance}}{\text{time}}$	$v = \dfrac{s}{t}$	$m\,s^{-1}$ metres per second	distance travelled per second
work done = force × distance moved in the direction of the force	$W = Fs$	J joules	energy transferred when a force results in motion
power $= \dfrac{\text{work done (energy transfer)}}{\text{time taken}}$	$P = \dfrac{W}{t}$	W watts	rate at which energy is transferred
efficiency $= \dfrac{\text{useful work done} \times 100}{\text{energy supplied}}$			percentage of supplied energy which is used usefully
density $= \dfrac{\text{mass}}{\text{volume}}$	$\rho = \dfrac{m}{V}$	$kg\,m^{-3}$	mass per unit volume
resistance $= \dfrac{\text{potential difference}}{\text{current}}$	$R = \dfrac{V}{I}$	Ω ohms	ratio of potential difference across a conductor to the current flowing through it
power = potential difference × current	$P = VI$	W watts	the rate at which energy is transferred
resistivity $= \dfrac{\text{resistance} \times \text{area}}{\text{length}}$	$\rho = \dfrac{RA}{l}$	Ω m ohm metre	the electrical resistance across a sample length 1 m, cross section 1 m^2

Solids

Definitions

Tensile strength: The force needed to break a sample of the material divided by its cross-sectional area.

Thermal conductivity: The rate of energy transfer through a cross section $1\,m^2$ when the temperature change is $1\,K$ for every metre of length.

Electrical conductivity: The current through a cross section of $1\,m^2$ when the potential difference is $1\,V$ for every metre of length.

SUBSTANCE	DENSITY	TENSILE STRENGTH	ELECTRICAL RESISTIVITY	ELECTRICAL CONDUCTIVITY	THERMAL CONDUCTIVITY	TYPE
units	$kg\,m^{-3}$	pascals (or $N\,m^{-2}$)	$\Omega\,m$	$\Omega^{-1}\,m^{-1}$	$W\,m^{-1}\,K^{-1}$	
Aluminium	2700	6 to 40×10^7	2.4×10^{-8}	4.2×10^7	200	crystalline
Copper	8940	2.2 to 4.3×10^8	1.6×10^{-8}	6.3×10^7	385	crystalline
Iron	7860	2.1×10^8	8.9×10^{-8}	1.1×10^7	80	crystalline
Lead	11350	1.5×10^7	1.9×10^{-7}	5.2×10^6	38	crystalline
Mild steel	7700	2.5×10^8	1.7×10^{-7}	5.9×10^6	60	crystalline
Stainless steel	7800	7 to 15×10^8	5.5×10^{-7}	1.8×10^6	25	crystalline
Oak timber	720	2.1×10^7	–	–	0.16	fibrous composite
Plasterboard	700 to 1300	2 to 5×10^6	–	–	0.18	amorphous
Common brick	1500 to 1800	Depends on joints	–	–	1.0	amorphous
Breeze block	1300 to 1500	Depends on joints	–	–	0.4	composite
Concrete	2200 to 2400	low – cracks unless reinforced	–	–	1.45	composite
Sheet glass	2460	3 to 9×10^7	2×10^{11}	5×10^{-12}	–	amorphous
Earthenware	2500	5.0×10^7 (bending test)	–	–	1.6	amorphous ceramic
Electrical porcelain	2500	1.05×10^8 (bending test)	–	10^{10} to 10^{12}	1.6	amorphous ceramic
Acrylic (e.g. Perspex)	1170 to 1200	5.5 to 7×10^7	10^{13}	10^{-13}	0.04 to 0.14	polymer
Nylon 6	1120 to 1140	4.5 to 9.0×10^7	–	10^9 to 10^{11}	0.25	polymer
Polythene (low density)	920	1.5×10^7	10^{14}	10^{-14}	0.33	polymer
Polythene (high density)	960	2.9×10^7	10^{14}	10^{-14}	0.45 to 0.52	polymer
Polychloroethane (PVC)	125 to 139	2 to 6×10^7	10^9 to 10^{14}	10^{-9} to 10^{-12}	0.12 to 0.17	polymer
Glass reinforced polyester	1500 to 2000	7.0 to 50×10^7	1.0 to 4.0×10^8	10^{13}	–	composite

Opposite properties of materials

SOFT MATERIALS	HARD MATERIALS
Lead Acrylic	Diamond Stainless steel

BRITTLE MATERIALS	TOUGH MATERIALS
Glass Ceramics Cast iron Concrete	Steel Polythene Copper Rubber

STIFF MATERIALS	FLEXIBLE MATERIALS
Steel Engineering brick Glass	Oak timber Polythene Glass reinforced polyester

TRANSPARENT	OPAQUE MATERIALS
Glass Diamond Water Acrylic	Steel Concrete

Melting and boiling points

SUBSTANCE	SYMBOL OR FORMULA	MELTING POINT /°C	BOILING POINT /°C	STRUCTURE
Metal elements				
Aluminium	Al	660	2350	giant, metallic
Gold	Au	1063	2707	giant, metallic
Iron	Fe	1540	2760	giant, metallic
Lead	Pb	327	1760	giant, metallic
Magnesium	Mg	650	1100	giant, metallic
Mercury	Hg	-39	357	giant, metallic
Sodium	Na	98	900	giant, metallic
Non-metal elements				
Bromine	Br_2	−7	59	molecular, covalent
Carbon (diamond)	C	3550	4827	giant, covalent
Carbon (graphite)	C	3720	(sublimes)	giant, covalent
Chlorine	Cl_2	−101	−34	molecular, covalent
Helium	He	−270	−269	monatomic gas
Hydrogen	H_2	−259	−253	molecular, covalent
Nitrogen	N_2	−210	−196	molecular, covalent
Oxygen	O_2	−219	−183	molecular, covalent
Silicon	Si	1410	2677	giant, covalent
Sulphur (monoclinic)	S	115	445	molecular, covalent
Inorganic compounds				
Aluminium oxide	Al_2O_3	2015	2980	giant, ionic
Ammonia	NH3	−77	−34	molecular, covalent
Carbon dioxide	CO_2	sublimes	−78	molecular, covalent
Sodium chloride	NaCl	808	1465	giant, ionic
Water	H_2O	0	100	molecular, covalent
Organic compounds				
Ethanol	C_2H_5OH	−114	78	molecular, covalent
Glucose	$C_6H_{12}O_6$	146	decomposes	molecular, covalent

A neutral (uncharged) atom can gain electric charge. Then we say that it becomes an ion.

Atoms turn into positive ions by losing electrons. The charge is single (+), double (2+), or triple (3+), depending on whether the atom loses one, two or three electrons. For example, Na^+, Mg^{2+}, Al^{3+}.

Atoms turn into negative ions by gaining electrons. The charge is single (–), or double (2–), depending on whether the atom gains one or two electrons. For example, Cl^-, O^{2-}.

Some ions are more complex and are made up of groups of atoms that, between them, have an electric charge.

POSITIVE IONS		NEGATIVE IONS	
NAME	FORMULA	NAME	FORMULA
Hydrogen	H^+	Chloride	Cl^-
Sodium	Na^+	Fluoride	F^-
Potassium	K^+	Hydroxide	OH^-
Ammonium	NH_4^+	Nitrate	NO_3^-
Calcium	Ca^{2+}	Oxide	O^{2-}
Copper	Cu^{2+}	Sulphate	SO_4^{2-}
Iron (III)	Fe^{3+}	Carbonate	CO_3^{2-}

CHEMICAL TESTS

Tests for metal ions

METAL ION	FLAME COLOUR
K^+	Pale mauve
Na^+	Bright yellow
Ca^{2+}	Orange–red
Cu^{2+}	Green with blue streaks
Mg^{2+}	No colour

Testing a solution

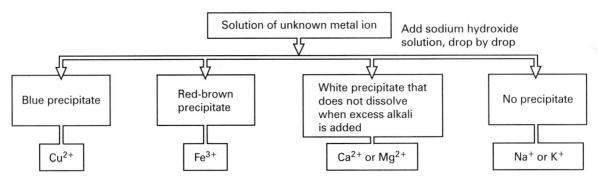

Tests for non-metal ions in salts

TEST	OBSERVATIONS	CONCLUSIONS
Add dilute hydrochloric acid to the solid salt	Gas turns limewater cloudy	Carbon dioxide from a carbonate
Make a solution of the salt. Acidify with nitric acid, then add a solution of silver nitrate	White precipitate	Silver chloride from a chloride
Take a fresh solution of the salt. Acidify with nitric acid, then add a solution of barium nitrate (or barium chloride)	White precipitate	Barium sulphate from a sulphate

Tests for gases

GAS	TESTS	RESULTS
Hydrogen	Burning splint	Burns with a small explosion (pop)
Oxygen	Glowing splint	Relights
Carbon dioxide	Limewater (solution of calcium hydroxide)	Turns milky white (precipitate of calcium carbonate)
Chlorine	Colour (blue litmus paper)	Yellow-green (bleached – may turn red first)
Ammonia	Smell (red litmus paper)	Pungent (turns blue)

Solubility of salts and hydroxides in water at room temperature

SOLUBLE IN WATER	INSOLUBLE IN WATER
All sodium, potassium and ammonium salts	
All nitrates	
Most chlorides and bromides	Silver and lead chlorides, bromides and iodides
Most sulphates	Lead sulphate, barium sulphate, calcium sulphate (which is slightly soluble and present in some natural waters)
Sodium, potassium and ammonium carbonates	Most other carbonates
Sodium and potassium hydroxides	
Ammonia solution (ammonium hydroxide)	
Calcium hydroxide is slightly soluble	Most other hydroxides

Selected elements, with atomic numbers, and relative atomic masses (to the nearest 0.5):

NAME	SYMBOL	ATOMIC NUMBER	RELATIVE ATOMIC MASS
aluminium	Al	13	27
barium	Ba	56	137.5
bromine	Br	35	80
calcium	Ca	20	40
carbon	C	6	12
chlorine	Cl	17	35.5
copper	Cu	29	63.5
fluorine	F	9	19
gold	Au	79	197
helium	He	2	4
hydrogen	H	1	1
iodine	I	53	127
iron	Fe	26	56
lead	Pb	82	207
magnesium	Mg	12	24.5
mercury	Hg	80	200.5
nitrogen	N	7	14
oxygen	O	8	16
phosphorus	P	15	31
potassium	P	15	39
silicon	Si	14	28
silver	Ag	47	108
sodium	Na	11	23
sulphur	S	16	32
zinc	Zn	30	65.5

Principle plant nutrient elements

ELEMENT	FUNCTION
Nitrogen	As a major constituent of protein it is needed for all plant growth
Phosphorus	A constituent of many proteins, fats and carbohydrates. Especially important in the ripening of fruits, the germination of seeds and root growth
Potassium	For good flower and fruit formation, photosynthesis and control of water loss
Calcium	For plant cell walls
Magnesium	A constituent of chlorophyll and so essential for photosynthesis

Nutrients for humans and other mammals

NUTRIENT	MAIN FUNCTION	FOOD SOURCES
Protein	For growth and repair of tissue	Meat, offal, fish, soya beans, cheese and eggs. Pulses, seeds, nuts and grains
Carbohydrates	For energy source	Cereals, potatoes, sugar, milk, root vegetables, fruits, nuts and seeds
Fats	For energy source	Butter, margarine, milk, egg yolk, nuts and seeds, meat, cooking fats and oils
Vitamin A	For growth of teeth, bones and skin, for resisting infection, and for good vision	Green vegetables, milk, butter, liver, fish liver oils
B vitamins	For metabolizing carbohydrates, proteins and fats. Helps to maintain a healthy nervous system	Yeast, wheatgerm, brown rice, leafy vegetables, walnuts
Vitamin C	For healing and for the efficient absorption of iron	Oranges, lemons, tomatoes, blackcurrants, fresh vegetables
Vitamin D	For health of bones and teeth	Fish liver oil, egg-yolk
Vitamin E	Protects membranes of cells	Fish liver oil, nuts, seeds, green leafy vegetables
Vitamin K	Aids blood clotting	Green leafy vegetables, yoghurt, peas, cauliflower, cereals
Calcium	For teeth, bones and muscle tone	Cheese, milk, fish with edible bones (sardines), lentils
Iron	For formation of red blood cells	Liver, sardines, dried fruits, rice, nuts
Phosphorus	For healthy teeth and bones	Present in nearly all foods
Iodine	For the thyroid gland to function	Onions, seafood, kelp, iodized salt
Sodium	To maintain balance of fluids	Salt, traces in seafood and plants

Human systems

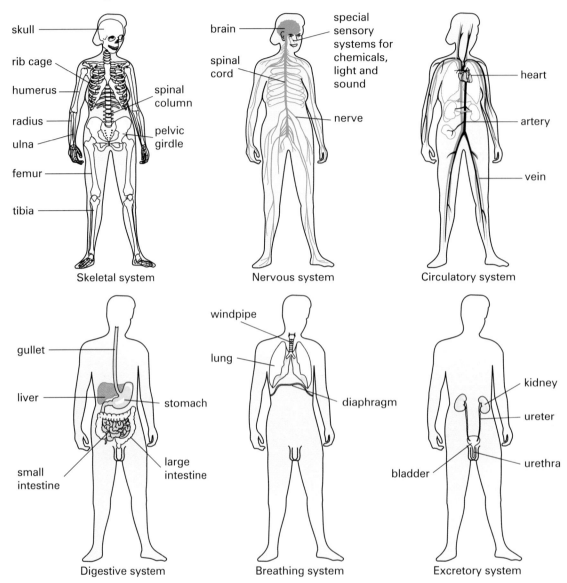

Skeletal system
- skull
- rib cage
- humerus
- radius
- ulna
- femur
- tibia
- spinal column
- pelvic girdle

Nervous system
- brain
- spinal cord
- special sensory systems for chemicals, light and sound
- nerve

Circulatory system
- heart
- artery
- vein

Digestive system
- gullet
- liver
- small intestine
- stomach
- large intestine

Breathing system
- windpipe
- lung
- diaphragm

Excretory system
- kidney
- ureter
- urethra
- bladder

Energy conversion rates for various activities

ACTIVITY	ENERGY CONVERSION RATE/W
Sleeping	70
Walking	250
Sitting reading	85
Standing up	160
Preparing a meal	100

ACTIVITY	ENERGY CONVERSION RATE/W
Ironing	300
Playing a piano	180
Swimming	340
Farm work	500
Playing football	600

Energy values of some foods

FOOD SOURCE	ENERGY VALUE /kJ PER 100 g
Dairy products	
Butter	3376
Cheese, cheddar	1600
Eggs	662
Margarine	3536
Milk, whole	320
Meat	
Bacon, lean	1044
Beef, lean	964
Chicken, cooked, no skin	480
Lamb, roast	1190
Fish	
Cod, raw	320
Sardines, canned in oil	964
Vegetables	
Bean sprouts	64
Cabbage	80
Chick peas	400
Kidney beans	400
Lentils, boiled	480
Lettuce	46
Peas	320
Potatoes, boiled	400
Tomatoes	64

FOOD SOURCE	ENERGY VALUE /kJ PER 100 g
Fruit	
Apple	160
Banana	402
Orange	160
Peach	160
Strawberry	160
Cereals	
Bread	1060
Cornflakes	1529
Naan bread	1105
Pasta	1608
Rice	1688
Sweet things	
Chocolate, milk	2412
Digestive biscuit	804
Ice cream	720
Jam	1204
Sugar	1768

Human factors

	AT REST	DURING EXERCISE
Pulse rate	70 times per minute	100+ times per minute
Heart rate	5 litres per minute	20+ litres per minute
Body temperature	35.9–37.8 °C	

Electrical and electronic circuit symbols

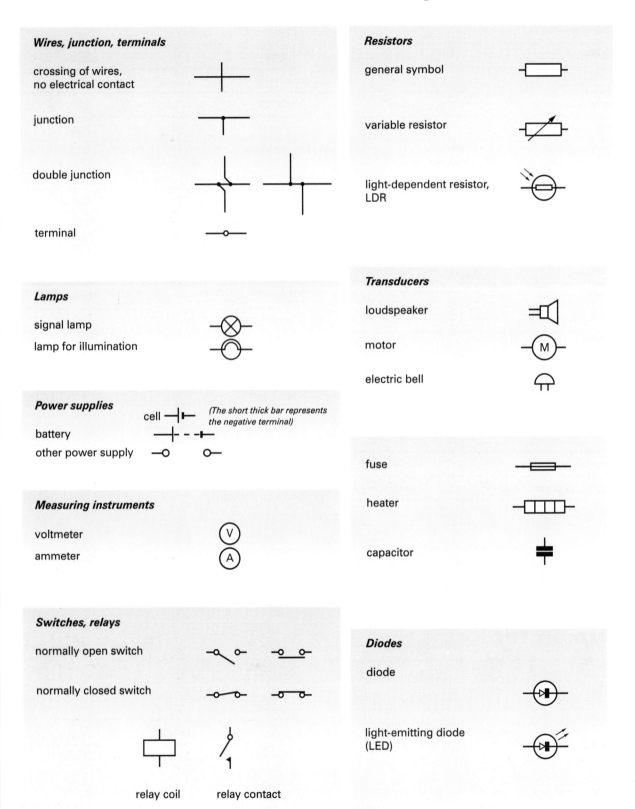

Wires, junction, terminals

crossing of wires,
no electrical contact

junction

double junction

terminal

Lamps

signal lamp

lamp for illumination

Power supplies

cell   *(The short thick bar represents
the negative terminal)*

battery

other power supply

Measuring instruments

voltmeter

ammeter

Switches, relays

normally open switch

normally closed switch

relay coil   relay contact

Resistors

general symbol

variable resistor

light-dependent resistor,
LDR

Transducers

loudspeaker

motor

electric bell

fuse

heater

capacitor

Diodes

diode

light-emitting diode
(LED)

Atoms and bonds

Some examples of the way molecules can be represented by models.

NAME	MOLECULAR FORMULA	STRUCTURAL FORMULA	BALL AND STICK MODEL	SPACE-FILLING MODEL
Hydrogen	H_2	H–H		
Hydrogen chloride	HCl	H–Cl		
Water	H_2O	$\begin{array}{c} O \\ H \quad\quad H \end{array}$		
Methane	CH_4	$\begin{array}{c} H \\ H-C-H \\ H \end{array}$		
Ethanol	C_2H_5OH	$\begin{array}{c} H \quad H \\ H-C-C-O-H \\ H \quad H \end{array}$		

Gender

female   male

Hazards

Warning signs are often fixed to doors or cupboards – they give warning of a hazard in the area. Signs in the laboratory include:

Hazardous chemicals must carry a warning label on the bottle. These labels include:

HIGHLY FLAMMABLE

RADIOACTIVE

RISK OF ELECTRIC SHOCK (DANGEROUS VOLTAGE)

EXPLOSIVE

OXIDIZING

CORROSIVE

DANGER

LASER RADIATION

NON-IONIZING RADIATION

HIGHLY FLAMMABLE

HARMFUL or IRRITANT

TOXIC

Hazards

A hazard is anything that can cause harm if things go wrong. Hazards include:

- chemicals (such as corrosive acids and alkalis, toxic gases and chemicals which cause cancer)
- high voltages (from the electricity mains and equipment with higher voltage such as TV sets)
- high temperatures (for example, in furnaces and flames)
- biological materials (such as infected blood, bacterial cultures and toxic organisms).

Risks

A risk is the chance (big or small) of harm actually being done when things go wrong (for example, risk of electric shock from faulty equipment).

Control of Substances Hazardous to Health Regulations (COSHH), 1988

Regulation 2: Definitions of substances hazardous to health

COSHH regulations apply to:

- substances which are toxic, harmful, corrosive or irritant
- substances which have maximum exposure limits
- substances which cause cancer, mutations or birth defects.

Substances hazardous to health are not just single chemical compounds, but also include mixtures of compounds, micro-organisms and allergens. The form of the substance matters, a substance which is harmless in lumps may be very hazardous when finely powdered.

Regulation 7: Preventing and controlling exposures

Employers have a duty to ensure that exposure of employees to substances hazardous to health is either prevented or adequately controlled.

Employers must do their best to prevent exposure by means such as:

- changing the method of working
- modifying the process to avoid hazardous by-products or wastes
- substituting a new substance which is less hazardous.

Where is it not possible to prevent exposure, employers should first try to control the hazard by methods which do not involve employees wearing protective clothing. This might involve enclosing the process, improving ventilation with fans and regular cleaning.

Personal Protective Equipment at Work Regulations, 1993

Personal protective equipment (PPE) includes clothing (such as aprons, gloves, safety helmets, and equipment (such as eye protectors, respirators). PPE should always be regarded as a last resort. Alternatives not requiring PPE should always be considered first.

Regulation 10: Proper use of protective equipment

PPE should only be used after adequate training. Employees have a duty to use the PPE provided as instructed by employers and to follow the guidance from the manufacturers.

Regulations 11: Loss and defects

Employees must take reasonable care of PPE provided and report any losses or defects to their employers as soon as possible.

Management of Health and Safety at Work Regulations, 1992

Regulation 7: Emergencies and danger areas

Employers need to establish procedures which mean that employees know what to do in an emergency – in case of fire, for example. Where a risk assessment has identified special risks, employers must make plans to cope with them too. The procedures must set out the roles of competent people with special responsibilities in an emergency. People are competent if they have sufficient training, experience or knowledge and other qualities to take responsibility in an emergency. Emergency procedures should be written down and form part of the induction and training of new workers.

A danger area is a place of work where the level of risk requires special precautions. The hazard may occupy the whole area (for example, a toxic gas) or be in just one place (such as exposed, live electric conductors). Employees must be trained to cope with the hazard before entering a danger area.

Electricity at Work Regulations, 1989

Nearly a quarter of all reportable electrical accidents involve portable equipment. Most of the accidents result in electric shocks. Others result in fires, in 1991, nearly 2000 fires were caused by faulty leads in the UK.

Portable appliances include any electrical equipment which is connected to the mains by a cable and is likely to be moved while connected to the supply. Extension leads are covered, as well as power packs, kettles and lamps.

Cost effective maintenance of portable electrical equipment should be based on a combination of:

► checks by the user
► visual inspection by a person appointed to do so
► inspection and tests (with a portable appliance tester) by a competent person.

Testing of portable equipment detects faults such as a broken earth wire or faulty insulation. At the same time the inspector should check that the correct fuse is in place and that the wires in the plug are connected to the right terminals.

Symbols for standards

The British Standards Institution tests products for quality, reliability and safety. They also monitor manufacturers' quality control systems. The 'kitemark' symbol may be displayed on products which comply with Standards set by the BSI.

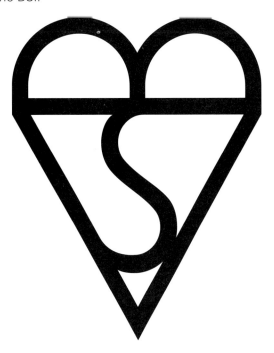

The CE mark on a product shows that it complies with relevant European Union Directives.

Index

Heinemann Educational Publishers,
a division of Heinemann Publishers (Oxford) Ltd,
Halley Court, Jordan Hill, Oxford, OX2 8EJ

OXFORD LONDON EDINBURGH
MADRID ATHENS BOLOGNA PARIS
MELBOURNE SYDNEY AUCKLAND SINGAPORE TOKYO
IBADAN NAIROBI HARARE GABORONE
PORTSMOUTH NH (USA)

© The Nuffield Foundation 1994

First published 1994

98 97 96 95 94
10 9 8 7 6 5 4 3 2 1

ISBN 0 435 63250 7
Designed and typeset by Gecko Ltd, Bicester, Oxon

Illustrated by Paul Adams, Gill Bishop, Gary Bullock, Neil Bulpitt, Gecko Ltd, Ian Heard,
Andrew McLaughlin, Dave Poole, Martin Sanders, Tony Wilkins and Mel Wright

Cover design by Threefold Design

Printed and bound in Great Britain by Bath Colour Books, Glasgow

The authors and publishers would like to thank the following
for permission to use photographs:

page 4 Paul Bryans; *page 5* T Eric Deeson, *B* Paul Bryans;
page 6 T Hutchison Library, *M and B* Hazel Rymer; *page 7*
Eric Deeson; *page 8 T* Chris Ridgers, *B* Topham Picture
Scource; *pages 9–10* Chris Ridgers; *page 14 TL* Ardea
Ltd/Graham Robertson, *ML* SPL/ David Guyon, *BL* SPL/ Will &
Deni McIntyre, *TR* Environmental Picture Library, *BR*
SPL/Physics Dept Imperial College London; *page 16* Chris
Ridgers; *pages 18–21* Roger Scruton; *page 21 BR* SPL/Eric
Grave; *pages 26–27* Paul Bryans; *page 28* Ardea Ltd; *page 29*
Heather Angel; *page 34* SPL/Hank Morgan; *page 35*
SPL/CNRI; *pages 36–38* Chris Ridgers; *page 38 second from
top* SPL/Claude Nuridsany & Marie Pervenou; *pages 39–40*
Jeremy Rowel Friers; *page 39* R Solo; *pages 44–45*
Matsushita Electric UK Ltd; *page 46* SPL/Julian Calder; *page
47* Tony Stone Worldwide; *page 50 T* Lawson Mardon Group,
M Jean Williamson/Mick Sharp, *B* Courtesy of Inchcape
Testing Services; *page 51 T* Peter Gould, *TM* Zefa, *BM* ACE
Photo Agency, *B* Allsport; *page 52* Courtesy of IBM; *page 53*
Division, Glaxo/G Tompkinson; *page 54 L* SPL/John
Kaprielian, *R* Network/Peter Jordan; *page 55* ACE Photo
Agency; *page 56* Building Research Establishment; *page 57*
T and B Builing Research Establishment, *M* Microscopix
Picture Library/Andrew Syred; *page 60 T* J Allan Cash Ltd,
M and B Roger Scruton; *page 61 T* J Keenlyside, *B* Roger
Scruton; *page 64* Peter Gould; *page 65* Philip Parkhouse;
page 66 TL and TM Popperfoto, *TR* Walter Gardiner
Photography, *M* Tony Stone Images, *B* Chris Ridgers;
pages 67–69 Chris Ridgers; *page 72* Hutchison Library;
page 73 Roger Scruton; *page 76 T* Chris Rodgers, *B* Graham
Trott; *pages 77–8* Philip Parkhouse; *page 79–83* Chris
Ridgers; *page 86 and 89* Allied Colloids; *page 87 T* SPL/Sheila
Tervy, *M* J Allan Cash Ltd, *B* Network Photographers/Mike
Abrahams; *page 88* ACE Photo Agency; *page 90 T* SPL/Guy
Gillette, B J Allan Cash Ltd; *page 92* SPL/Simon Fraser;

page 94 T Tony Stone Worldwide, B Givaudan-Roure; *page 95*
Givaudan-Roure; *page 98* SPL/Phil Jude; *page 99* Roger Scruton;
pages 102–3 Peter Gould; *pages 104–7* SPL; *page 104 B and
page 107 B* Collections/Anthea Sieve King; *pages 110–113*
Paul Bryans; *page 117 and 119* Allsport; *pages 122–3 and
125* Franta Provaznik; *page 124 T* Stoke Mandeville,
L SPL/Art Stein, *R* SPL/Tim Malyon & Paul Biddle; *page 128*
Courtesy of Johnson Matthey Chemicals/Peter Thorne;
page 131 SPL/Andrew Syred; *page 132 L* ACE Photo Agency,
R BPL Photographic Services; *page 133* Environmental
Picture Library; *pages 136–7* Chris Ridgers; *pages 140–41*
University of Nottingham; *page 144 L* ACE Photo Agency,
R and B SPL/Hank Morgan; *page 145 L* SPL/Stevie Grand,
R SPL/Andrew McClenghan, *B* Hutchison Library; *page 146*
J Allan Cash; *page 147* Peter Gould; *pages 148–150 T* x4
Patsie Stafford-Johnson, *page 150 B* x3 Carl Wheatly;
page 151 Chris O'Reilly.
Cover photo: Science Photo Library/Shirley Richards

The authors and publishers would like to thank the following
for permission to reproduce copyright material:

page 11 *The Daily Mirror* for article of 22 May 1992; page 12
The Lancet, "Mortality from tobacco in developed countries:
indirect estimation from national vital statistics" by R Peto,
AD Lopez, J Boreham, Michael Thun, C Heath, 23 May 1992;
page 13 The Imperial Cancer Research Fund, press release of
22 May 1992; page 17 the Controller of Her Majesty's
Stationery Office for extract from "Code of practice for the
prevention of infection in clinical laboratories and postmortem
rooms" 1978; page 182 BSI Kitemark used with kind
permission of the British Standards Institution.

The publishers have made every effort to trace the copyright
holders, but if they have inadvertently overlooked any, they
will be pleased to make the necessary arrangements at the
first opportunity.